D0626900

JULY, *1863*

JULY,
1863

* * * * * * * *

IRVING WERSTEIN

F
128
.44
.W38

JULIAN MESSNER, INC.
NEW YORK, N.Y.

Published by JULIAN MESSNER, INC.
8 West 40 Street, New York 18

Published simultaneously in Canada
by THE COPP CLARK PUBLISHING CO. LIMITED

Copyright © Irving Werstein, 1957

Printed in the United States of America
Library of Congress Catalog Card No. 57-10511

This book is for
Goldie and Ceil

Author's Note

This book is a re-creation of the five turbulent days in July, 1863, when mobs raged through the streets and blood was spilled in the heart of New York City. This was the time of the Draft Riots, when a desperate, underprivileged mob lashed out in anger and hatred at the provisions of a conscription law which exempted a man who had three hundred dollars to buy his way out.

But the uprising, begun as a protest, reached perilous and insurrectionary proportions, turning into a carnival of persecution and bigotry. The draft was forgotten in the carnage of looting, raping and arson. The mobs turned their venom against the helpless Negroes and committed great violence against them, not only because their skins were black, but also because the Negroes were in competition for jobs on the docks and in the factories. The rioters used the disorders as an excuse to attempt the destruction of their economic rivals.

Certain developments during the course of the rioting have led to the theory that they were, in part, at least, fomented and stirred up by Confederate agents and Southern sympathizers. Skilled rabble rousers did agitate the mobs and incite them to violence. Some trained, armed groups were operating with the mobs in the beginning of the riots. Controversy has always surrounded the role played by such men as Ben and Fernando Wood. *The New York Times* of July 16, 1863, said:

"We have no doubts that there are other men, agents direct from Richmond, now in this city, who are using both energy and money in feeding the flames that have for three days darkened and for three nights reddened the sky of New York."

I do not claim that the conspirators pictured in this re-creation, with the exception of John Andrews, really existed. Captain Ross Lane is based on a mysterious young man who led the attack on the Union Steam Works the afternoon of July 14 and commanded a group of disciplined men armed with muskets who moved and fought in military formation. The man was killed in the fore of the battle and his body spirited away by his followers. Before his corpse was recaptured by the rioters, police discovered he was wearing fine linen and expensive underclothing beneath his grimy work clothes. Had his identity been learned much more might have been known about the leaders of the riot. Nothing was ever found out about the men who followed him into battle like toughened and seasoned veterans; they might well have been Confederate volunteers hidden by Southern sympathizers until they were needed.

Certain incidents have been dramatized, but this book is essentially a factual recounting of the terrible events during the second week of July, 1863, only seven days after Gettysburg.

The speeches recorded here were made by the people indicated. The telegrams and military orders are taken verbatim from the records. I have given certain dialogue to real people like Commissioner Acton, Governor Seymour, General Brown, Mayor Opdyke and others. Their actions are based on newspaper accounts, eyewitness reports and descriptions of them in memoirs, diaries and biographies.

Many people have helped me with advice and encouragement. I wish to thank my friend Jay Williams of Redding, Connecticut, for his guidance. This book would not have been possible without the unselfish and expert assistance of Sylvester Vigilante and Sylvan W. McHenry of the New-York Historical Society, Ivor D. Avellino and Robert Hug of the New York Public Library, and the entire staff of the American History Room in the New York Public Library.

To these kind and hospitable friends in England, where part

of this book was written, I am grateful: Minna Cagan, Anne Rome, Kay Cummins, Risdon and Marjorie Couch, Tudor and Maureen Evans, Leslie and Jean Seed, all of London, and Ken and Una Bowden, of Pool-in-Wharfedale, Yorkshire. I wish to express gratitude to friends in Florence, Italy, where I also worked on *July, 1863*, especially Primo and Clara Di Vito, and Adriano and Nella Boni.

To my wife who went along every step of the way and spent many hours searching through the streets of New York City with me for landmarks of another day, my affectionate thanks.

I. W.

Florence, London, New York
1955–1957

There is no grievance that is a fit object of redress by mob law.—

Abraham Lincoln, address, Young Men's Lyceum, Springfield, Illinois, January 27, 1837.

PRELUDE

Saturday, July 11, 1863

Prelude

On March 3, 1863, in the third spring of the Civil War, President Abraham Lincoln signed the National Conscription Act—and with his signature set the stage for the bloodiest uprising in the turbulent history of New York City.

Briefly, the National Conscription Act was a law that provided for the enrollment of all males between the ages of eighteen and forty-five for military service. It set up Provost Marshal offices in designated Enrollment Districts and stipulated that at an unspecified date, the draft would be carried out under the direction of the various Provost Marshals. A complicated system of quotas was evolved for each area. The names of enrollees would be placed in a huge lottery wheel and drawn on until each district's quota was filled.

The draft law was violently attacked all over the country. In New York, Democratic newspapers declared that it was "tyranny of the worst sort, worthy of the most ruthless despot" and anti-administration politicians took to the stump against it with all the hot air at their command. They called it "un-American" and unconstitutional.

Ignoring the objectors, the government officials headed

by Provost General James B. Fry went on about their business. Preparations were made to enroll all eligible males.

Actually, the draft law was neither tyranny nor despotism. It was simply an ambiguous law set up by a Congress which was frightened that the Volunteer system could no longer keep the Union Army up to its required strength. There were many flaws in the Act—the worst being a special clause which permitted exemption from service for any man who paid the sum of three hundred dollars to the Provost Marshal or furnished a substitute at the time he was called.

While three hundred dollars was no hardship for a wealthy man or a moderately well-to-do shopkeeper or farmer, the sum was a fortune for the average workingman. If he was lucky, a laborer earned twenty dollars a week, but it was usually far less. In 1863, a dollar did not stretch far. Living costs had doubled since the beginning of the war in '61. Milk, bread, and other staples had soared in price, while roast beef, which cost eight cents a pound before the fall of Fort Sumter, now sold for sixteen cents. Eggs, which had been twelve and a half cents for thirteen, now cost twenty-five cents for an even dozen. Obviously, not many factory workers or day laborers could buy their way out of the draft.

In New York City further animosity was aroused by the Emancipation Proclamation on January 1, 1863; a huge population of Irish immigrants were already in desperate competition with free Negroes for unskilled jobs. Artful Copperheads told the Irish that this was a war "to free the nigger," and painted a dire picture of a city swarming with freed slaves who would glut the labor market.

Named by loyal Unionists after the deadly snake, the Copperheads were Southern sympathizers. There was much Copperhead activity in New York City, where many wealthy and prominent businessmen and manufacturers, shut off by the war from their sources of Southern cotton, were bitterly resentful. The majority of these Copperheads were Democrats and their activity ranged from full-scale sabotage to passive resistance to wartime measures.

Ben and Fernando Wood were leaders of the movement. Ben, editor of the most widely read paper in New York, **The Daily News,** kept just this side of sedition in his editorials. **The News** served, too, as a medium for Confederate spies and agents to communicate with each other in code via the paper's personal columns.

Fernando, former Mayor, was the initiator of agitation to have New York City secede from the state and be declared an open port. He came up with this plan at the beginning of the war. After his defeat as Mayor, he was elected to Congress and was a most vociferous opponent of Lincoln and his administration, openly expressing his Copperhead sentiments.

The mass of immigrants who had fled to the United States during the potato famines in the early fifties had no desire to fight in a war for which they could feel no sympathy. The great bulk of the Irish lived in unrelieved misery, in squalid tenements and disease-infested shanties. Earning a living was precarious for these untrained, unskilled people. They scrambled for marginal jobs as longshoremen, hod carriers, chimney sweeps, dustmen, porters, bootblacks and carters. They were constantly pitted against Negroes in the struggle for existence. Vicious fights were common on the docks where Irish and Negro strove for longshore work which paid one dollar and a half for a nine-hour day.

This meager livelihood for the laborer had continued for some years until, in 1861, the war brought new factories and new industry to the city. The labor sources were drained by the Army, leaving the harbor jammed with shipping. At last, there was work for all—and then, after only two years of tenuous prosperity, the immigrants were faced with the draft. They resented giving up hard-won jobs, resented bitterly the fact that their old antagonists, the Negroes, were not even subject to the draft. Hatreds flared and scarcely a day went by without fists, knives and even pistols beeing used on the docks as the labor war rose to new violence.

Miserable as the lot of the Irish was, anything seemed better than marching off to war and getting one's head blown off. It was a "rich man's war and a poor man's fight": who wanted to get killed for the "niggers"?

Opposition to the draft took many forms. Some used direct action. Enrollment officers were beaten up and all sorts of sabotage was used to hinder their work. Men gave false names and in one district there were aliases like: Tom Snooks, John Doe, Richard Roe, Jeremy Diddler, John Smith, John Brown, and Jesus Christ.

Commenting on this, **The Tribune** said on June 25, 1863:

> "The rendering of false names to the enrolling officers may be looked on as a joke, but there is such a thing as carrying a joke too far and the laugh, in the end, may come in on the other side. . . ."

Every night, saloons and grogshops in slum neighborhoods were filled with men who openly boasted they would never be drafted without a fight. Others who opposed the draft met in secret, and their plans went far beyond hindering an objectionable law. Whispers of their intentions leaked out; rumors that there would be a general uprising, an armed revolt, and the seizure of New York City, to force the Lincoln government into surrender.

Actually, no one believed such fanciful gossip. The average citizen hoped that Washington would simply forget "the whole stupid draft business," and for a time it seemed that this would happen. The cumbersome draft machinery appeared to have stalled.

Meanwhile, opportunists took advantage of the situation. Evading the draft became a profession. New York newspapers carried many advertisements like this one:

> "How to avoid the draft! On receipt of $1.00 will send instructions how to avoid the draft, or get exempt, if drafted, at the cost of just 37½ cents. Lawyer, 129 Spring Street, Station A, New York City."

But after weeks of false alarms and much hedging, the draft was definitely ordered in the 8th and 9th Districts of New York City, in several districts of Brooklyn, some upstate New York cities, New Jersey, and New England. It was scheduled to start at 9:00 a.m. on July 11, 1863—a Saturday.

In New York City, the drawings were to be held at 1190 Broadway, near 29th Street, under the supervision of Provost Marshal Benjamin Mannierre, for the 8th District; and at 677 Third Avenue, at the corner of 46th Street, Charles Jenkins, Provost Marshal, for the 9th District.

The announcement was anticlimactic and after all the shouts and whispers of violence, little reaction was felt when the morning papers on Friday, July 10, carried the news. Editorial comment was brief, even in the anti-administration sheets. Some papers actually made no editorial mention of the draft at all.

Even the most wishful thinker gave in to reality at 9:00 on the overcast, sultry morning of Saturday, July 11, when Provost Marshal Charles Jenkins strode briskly to the table on which stood the revolving drum holding the names of 9th District enrollees.

The draft office was located in a row of recently erected four-story brick and frame buildings. The upper floors were tenements and the Marshal's office was flanked on one side by Robert Pettigrew's carriage shop and on the other by a lager beer saloon.

The room in which the proceedings were held was a large one, divided in the center by a wooden railing, behind which Jenkins conducted his business. A crowd of about two hundred persons, mostly men and boys from the adjacent working-class neighborhood, filled the office. A detail of policemen from the 19th Precinct commanded by Captain Galen Porter guarded the premises.

The police had little to do except watch the activities. The crowd was loud and nervously boisterous but in high spirits. The onlookers made coarse jokes and jostled playfully while awaiting the drawing and the calling of the drafted men's names. At a few minutes after 9:00, Jenkins made a sign. His chief clerk, Charles H. Carpenter, was blindfolded, and George W. Southwick, another clerk, turned a crank that set the drum spinning.

When the wheel stopped, Carpenter reached into the mouth of the drum and pulled out a slip of paper. For the first time in the history of the United States an American citizen was being conscripted into the Army. Jenkins took the paper from his clerk, unfolded it, and in a clear voice read the name and address of the draftee.

"William Jones, 46th Street, corner Tenth Avenue," Jenkins announced. The draft was official. Jones, a laborer, had the unpleasant distinction of being the first man drafted in New York City.

The spectators responded with crude humor. "Poor Willie!" a man shouted, pretending to weep and wiping his eyes with a large soiled bandana.

"How are you, Willie?" they cried derisively.

"Oh, our Willie's gone for to be a soldier!" a man jeered.

Jenkins smiled faintly as the abashed recruit, who happened to be present, shuffled and squirmed uneasily. His friends whacked the conscript on the shoulder and shook his hand. The Marshal was greatly relieved by the crowd's reaction. Compared to what might have happened, this festive air was a welcome surprise.

The drawing continued. Each name was greeted with jovial shouts. At noon, Jenkins closed for the day. He had drawn several hundred names without incident. The crowd straggled out of his office and into the beer saloon next door. Because the initial phases of the draft had gone peacefully, many smugly believed that no trouble was in the offing. The prophets and criers of doom had been all wrong, they said. New Yorkers were loyal and law-abiding citizens—not Copperhead troublemakers. Indiana and Ohio might be hotbeds of treason—but not New York, the greatest city in the Union!

RUMBLINGS

Sunday, July 12, 1863

S INCE sunrise, a promise of rain threatened to ruin the Sunday holiday-making of New Yorkers on July 12. Dull, gray clouds filtered the sunshine. Thunder rumbled testily in the bowels of the clouds. The day was hot and clammy, but the city folk were determined that nothing would hamper their pleasures.

Thousands found some relief from the heat in Central Park. They strolled on shaded paths and relaxed in secluded spots. The carriage roads winding through the cool woods were crowded with pleasure vehicles. Boats flying red and blue pennants glided about the lagoon. Laughing girls twirled parasols as their escorts plied the oars.

Strollers meandered along Fifth Avenue and visited the Croton Reservoir on 42nd Street to climb the broad high walls and view the panorama of the city. From the walls of the reservoir they could see the ships at anchor in both rivers, and all the way north toward Harlem, Yorkville, and Manhattanville there was rolling, green country and pleasant farmland, although the area in the vicinity of 42nd Street, west of Sixth Avenue, was dotted with miserable squatter shacks and goatherds' shanties.

The city was laid out to 137th Street but there was little north of 57th, the main residential and business districts being south of 23rd Street. Along lower Fifth Avenue, Stuyvesant Square, Madison Square and Gramercy Park were the fine homes of the wealthy; but beyond, lay miserable slums, the worst of which was the Five Points district, formed by the intersection of Pearl, Worth, Baxter and Water Streets.

New Yorkers enjoyed their holiday in many ways. Some traveled across the river to Brooklyn or out to the rural Eastern District to picnic. Others ventured to Staten Island or went to the

Elysian Fields in Weehawken to spend the day. Uptown, in Jones' Woods, the German-American groups held their annual gala Liederkranz Festival, complete with tootling bands and gymnastic exhibitions by Turn-Verein Clubs.

But not all New Yorkers were enjoying the Sabbath's serenity. The Sunday newspapers carried the names of the drafted men—most of them poor laborers and mechanics. The sight of these names in print was a sober reminder that the draft had become a reality. In the 9th District, east of Fifth Avenue in the forties, crowds of Sunday loungers gathered on street corners and in saloons to talk over the situation. The talk grew louder and burst into argument. And in the slums, the sordid streets of tenements and shanties, resentments seethed. Central Park was peaceful—but it was two miles from Water Street, from the stinking morass of dingy dwellings and crumbling shacks.

As daylight waned, agitated crowds thronged the streets of the poorer neighborhoods. Men drank cheap whisky. They grew drunk and mean and cursed the draft; and the women who mingled with them were far more vehement than the men. They called the drawings a lottery of death.

"Don't go off like damned sheep. Stand and fight!" they cried.

"Drafted men get no bounty. How are we to put bread on the table with you in the army?" they shrieked at drink-befuddled men.

"Damn it! Are you going to let your wives and young'uns starve while the niggers stay home and grow fat?" they argued.

The day passed and the drinking became heavier. Tempers snapped. Fist fights broke out. And through the increasing turmoil one hatred persisted. The "niggers" were to blame for everything. Get rid of the "niggers" and the lousy government that made the draft. The rich wanted the war. Down with the draft!

Drunken men glared with reddened eyes and lurched about in helpless fury. The day was ending in ugliness. . . .

George Opdyke, 76th Mayor of New York City, was a millionaire before his fifty-eighth birthday. Not only was he wealthy, but also a Republican, a Union Leaguer and the father of six children. He had made his money through shrewd dealings, numbering among his holdings a prosperous textile importing company, a chain of mercantile establishments, several clothing factories, and a silent partnership in a factory known as Marston and Company. He took no active part in the firm, leaving its operation to his son-in-law, Thomas Marston. It was, however, no secret that he was a heavy investor in the enterprise which conducted its business in an old, ramshackle five-story wooden building on Second Avenue at 21st Street.

The three upper floors of the structure were used as a State Armory. Several thousand carbines and quantities of ammunition were stored there. The lower levels housed the workshop and offices of Marston and Company. Before the war the concern had manufactured various types of wire—but since '61, the plant had turned out carbines. In fact, the very weapons stored in the upstairs armory were Marston products.

Opdyke was a self-made man who constantly strove to conceal his plebian origins. He was not a son of wealth. His father had owned a small country store at a New Jersey village crossroads. Now, this successful son of a simple countryman lived like a patrician in an elegant house at 79 Fifth Avenue, drank aged brandy and smoked tailor-made Havana cigars.

In the late afternoon of this Sunday, the Mayor stood at an open French window, moodily staring at his carefully tended garden and smoking one of his special cigars. He was a man satisfied with himself—feeling certain that he had cause to be content. During the mayoralty election in November, he had soundly defeated the wily Democrat, Fernando Wood. Under his administration, the city government was being piloted honestly, at least, if not smoothly. Petty annoyances galled the Mayor. The office-holding Democrats were constantly sabotaging him, guided by the former Mayor. Many of Fernando's henchmen still sat in the Board of Aldermen and knew how to give the Mayor a bad time.

But at the moment, Opdyke wasn't concerned about Wood and his crew. The insistent talk that trouble would still result from the draft gnawed at him. Nothing had happened, but he would have felt more secure if all the troops—militia and regulars—that had fought in the battle of Gettysburg were safely back home to handle any unpleasantness. Of course, New York had a capable police force which would make short shrift of malcontents. There was really nothing to worry about. The whispers and rumors of uprisings and outbreaks over the draft were so much poppycock—yet according to the Chief of Detectives, Sergeant John Young, something unsavory was stirring in the lower wards. . . .

Only a half hour earlier, Young had called on the Mayor with disturbing news. Opdyke pulled on his cigar as he recalled Young's visit.

"Your Honor, they're fixing for trouble with all this talk against the draft," Young had said. "I've had reports——"

"Damn your reports, Sergeant," Opdyke replied irritably. "Facts are facts. We had no trouble yesterday, did we? Why should there be any tomorrow, when the drafting continues?"

"The people have had a whole day to mull it over, sir. They've been doing a lot of drinking, and whisky doesn't mix well with bad tempers," Young said.

Opdyke was an impressive looking man nearly six feet tall. He had a way of crushing subordinates with a stare of gelid disapproval. "Sergeant, don't be a fool. We're in no danger. None at all."

"I'm sorry to disagree, sir. My detectives have been out all day long and the reports they've sent in are not at all reassuring," Young said doggedly.

"Well, sir, what do you want me to do?" Opdyke asked.

"Have General Sandford gather all the available militia in the city, and. . . ."

"Sergeant, that's been done. There is no militia to speak of—but General Sandford has mobilized whatever forces he could. Tell me, Sergeant, what reports have you received ominous enough to bring you here?"

"Down in the 5th Ward, half a dozen Negroes were beaten—and three or four shacks were set afire by a crowd," Young said.

"My good fellow, we have fires in this city every night—and capable fire volunteers to deal with them. As for the attacks on colored persons, that too, as you know, is a common occurrence, unfortunately. I believe you're unduly alarmed."

Opdyke smiled at the bulky detective. He clapped him on the shoulder in a friendly manner, walked to his desk and opened an ornately hand-tooled Florentine leather cigar box which he extended to Young.

"Here, Sergeant, have a cigar," he said. The gesture was one of dismissal. Young took a cigar, bade the Mayor good night and left. After the detective was gone, Opdyke pondered about his visit. He was certain he had behaved properly, yet there was some doubt in his mind. Had he sent Young away because it was easier to hide from the truth? Was he, after all, afraid to face the possibility that the whispers of open resistance to the draft would materialize?

He shook off such thoughts. He was not a man to shirk his duties or his responsibilities. Young had misinterpreted the signs. The Mayor felt a spark of resentment toward the detective for bothering him, giving him these uncomfortable moments. He was glad Mrs. Opdyke and the children were off in the Adirondacks for their summer holiday. It would have upset Mrs. Opdyke had she heard Young.

A full-toned grandfather's clock in the entrance hall chimed six times. Opdyke stepped away from the window. Time to meet Ben Mannierre for dinner. They would have a lavish meal at the

Metropolitan Hotel and afterwards go to Niblo's Gardens to see a good melodrama, *The Duke's Motto*. The Mayor looked forward to the evening with relish. Not that Opdyke didn't miss his family. But, he did not mind that the draft had forced him to remain in the city; a bachelor evening with Ben occasionally was a desirable change. Moreover, the city's Chief Executive belonged at his post in a time of even potential unrest. He wasn't like Horatio Seymour, the Governor. In Opdyke's opinion, the Governor had behaved shamefully, skedaddling off to the Jersey shore for the week end, after only a hurried inspection of the city's harbor defenses upon his arrival from Albany on Friday.

Seymour opposed the draft, as everyone knew. He had left no one in doubt about his feeling. But, even so, he should have remained in New York. His action would do the Governor little good politically. Quite frankly, Opdyke did not like the Governor. Seymour was intelligent and personable, but there was a precise coldness about the man that kept one at arm's length. Opdyke never expected Seymour to be his close friend; the Governor, after all, was a Democrat. But, unlike many of Seymour's political foes, Opdyke did not believe the Governor was either disloyal or a Copperhead. When the call had come for New York troops to be sent into Pennsylvania, Seymour had sent more regiments then the State's actual quota. This was not the behavior of a traitor.

At any rate, Opdyke intended to relax and forget the cares of office for this one evening. He placed several cigars in the breast pocket of his finely tailored linen jacket and left the house. He was whistling as he paused at the wrought-iron gate and gazed out over sumptuous Fifth Avenue. He stepped out into the street. Beckoning to his coachman, he paid no attention to the distant clangor of fire bells downtown in the direction of the Negro district.

Fire Engine Company No. 33 was located in a frame building on Broadway near West 58th Street. It was an undeveloped, rural neighborhood with farms and scattered cottages. The volunteers of this station were noted rowdies feared even by the toughest Five Points gangsters. Everyone gave the "Black Joke" bunch a wide berth. They had derived their odd name from the sleek, shiny black, hand-hauled pumper engine they pulled to fires, kept gleaming by its devoted crew, and incongruously christened "Black Joke."

When the bells sounded, the "Black Joke" crew, led by burly, bushy-haired Pete Masterson, the foreman, was ready to fight a fire, sail into a free-for-all, or hold a wild, all-night party with a bevy of Prince Street whores.

Masterson was a shady character who dealt in dirty politics and quasi-legal businesses with disreputable associates, most of whom were leaders of Five Points gangs.

Usually, the men hung around the firehouse on a hot summer's night, polishing equipment, swapping yarns and drinking beer, freely supplied by Masterson. On this steaming July night there was no joviality in the station house. No laughter rattled the windows. The men drank bad, raw whisky. Masterson sat sulking in a corner, his thick brows drawn into a sullen frown. His men stood about him in a semicircle and the atmosphere was one of brooding.

They passed the whisky jug around in menacing silence. One man took a slug and wiped his lips with the back of his hand. He said, "We ain't going to let them get away with it, Pete."

"That's the truth, Danny," another man said as he reached for the jug.

"The gall of the bastards! Drafting Pete Masterson. Why, the nigger-loving Republican sons of bitches! I'll break that scrawny bastard Jenkins in half," a man cried.

Masterson held up a big-knuckled hand and they fell silent.

"Lads, you've got to do more than fix Jenkins. You've got to go a lot further," he said, meaningfully.

"How's that, Pete?" a fireman asked.

"When that damned Marshal's office opens tomorrow, I want you lads to be there and I want to make certain no man's name is ever drawn from that wheel again, understand?" Masterson said.

"We'll wreck the place for you, Pete," a man said.

"Now, lads, you ain't doing this for me," Masterson grinned. "It's for the good of the nation. A hell of a soldier I'd make. So when you bust up that wheel and tear up the drafting lists, you'll be serving the Union, won't you?"

He threw back his head and laughed. The others joined him and their guffawing shook the windowpanes and echoed over that peaceful neighborhood until cows grazing nearby looked up toward the fire station with great, puzzled, gentle eyes.

. . . 2

ABOUT the time Mayor Opdyke was dining on roast pheasant in the Grand Salon of the Metropolitan Hotel, at Broadway and Spring Street, and the "Black Joke" men were making their plans, a broad-shouldered six-footer with red hair and a full beard was standing at the bar of a saloon in Allen Street. Men wearing dirty shirts, rumpled trousers and scuffed working shoes crowded the dingy place. They noisily gulped beer and wolfed chunks of meat and succulent clams at the free lunch counter. When the red-haired man spoke, they eyed him with respect, admiring his pressed white linen suit, his Panama straw hat and the gold ruby ring that glittered on the little finger of his right hand. They listened to him raptly.

"Damn it, lads, you're free white men! Can't you see they're gulling you? You're free men—not hogs to be butchered! This draft must be crushed. You're the only ones who can do it!" He spoke in the ringing tones of a trained orator.

"Now you're talking chicken!" a small, shifty-eyed man cried. "The rich bastards want the war. Not us!" His shoe-button eyes flicking across the faces that had turned suddenly to him, he pointed to the speaker and cried, "Listen to him, buckos! It's worth your ear when John Andrews speaks!"

Andrews bowed slightly. "Thank you, my friend. I'm flattered that you know my name."

"Who ain't heard of John Andrews?" the small man cried.

The redhead made a sweeping gesture. "These fine lads, I'm sure, don't know me. I am not famous. But, friends, I'm one who knows what's good for the working class. I'm no Gramercy Park plug hat with three hundred dollars to buy out of the draft. I'm one of you!" He held up his white, manicured hands. The ruby reflected the gaslight. "I've dug ditches with these hands and hauled crates on the docks, like you. I'm one of you!" he repeated.

"That's the blarney! How come you're togged out like a dude?" an incredulous voice called.

"Worked on the docks, did you? Not with them mitts, you didn't!" a gnarled longshoreman cried.

"Sure, what are you feedin' us?" a loud voice asked.

"Friends, you've a right to talk that way. You're right to question me." Andrews turned to face the crowd. "Yes, I wear linen and broadcloth, instead of denim. My hands are soft and white while yours are calloused with honest toil. As a young man, I put in nine hours on the docks like any of you—every day. But

I went to sea, lads—and I studied the law and pulled myself up the ladder a bit. I made some money and I know the feel of a damask cloth and the taste of good wines, but John Andrews has never forgotten his people—the workers! My heart is with you, lads! My heart, lads! And that's why I can't stand idly and keep silent while that baboon in the White House steals the birthright of every free-born American workingman! Conscription is the tool of tyrants, Prussian Kings, Russian Czars, British monarchs! It's not for Americans!" He pounded the bar. "Were this a war to defend our homeland, not a man of you would hesitate to spill his blood to defend what he holds dear. But it's not a war to save our homes—it's an evil war for evil purposes! It's a war of oppression against white Southerners and to free the nigger! Free niggers—the black savages lusting for our women will roam the streets! No woman will be safe—nor any man! Is that what you want? Do you want to spill your blood so the niggers can be free?" Andrews finished excitedly, thoroughly moved by his own performance.

The listeners applauded and shouted, "No! No!"

A man rushed forward to pump Andrews by the hand. "That's the talk we need! That's the talk!"

The speaker took a handkerchief from his pocket, removed his hat and wiped the leather band inside the crown. His beard was damp with sweat and drops of perspiration dotted his ruddy forehead. He peered into the faces that encircled him, mopped his brow, drew a deep breath and clapped the hat back on his head again.

"It's hot tonight, but I'll promise you it'll be a damned sight hotter on the skirmish line with Minié balls zipping by your ears. And that's where you'll be soon enough unless you smash this rotten draft," Andrews said.

He glanced around the smoky room and spotted a young man who wore an army cap and a dirty blue army tunic which had several buttons missing. Andrews pointed to him and cried,

"Don't take my word. Here's a lad who knows far more than I do about war!"

"You can say that again, mister," the youth said, pushing his way toward Andrews. He was in his early twenties. Buck teeth protruded under his upper lip and wispy tufts of scraggly, straw colored hair hung from beneath the bent greasy cap on which the Maltese cross of the 5th Corps was still sewn.

He faced Andrews. "You're talking sense, bucko. We've got to stop the draft. These lads might as well die fighting at home as in some stinking Virginia swamp." Turning to the men, he said, "Listen to me, everybody! Listen! I've seen it all." He tapped himself on the chest with a dirty forefinger. "I'm still carrying a Reb ball, here. Got it at Antietam. And lots of my comrades, God rest 'em, got worse. And for what, friends? For what? For the dirty niggers, that's for what. Go out and save the Union they told us. All right. We fought and we bled. And some of us died. For the Union? No! For the nigger! For the war profiteer! And they'll make you do the same! The draft'll get you. Then what will become of your wives and your children? Who'll feed 'em when you're six feet under, with a bullet through your guts?"

A growling sound went up from the men. They shuffled from foot to foot and clutched their beer mugs, fear and hatred in their throats.

The yellow-haired youth shook both fists. His lips drew back in a snarl as he shouted, "The niggers! That's what this war is about! Go on and let yourselves be killed for 'em, if you will. But if you was men—you'd rise up and do something about it!"

"What can we do?" the little, sharp-eyed man asked.

"I'll tell you what to do," Andrews said, stepping in front of the ex-soldier. "You must smash this draft!"

"How?" a voice demanded.

"Are you ready to fight for your rights, for your own lives and those of your women and children?" Andrews asked.

"Yes! Yes!" the men shouted.

"Yes, you say? Then prove it. Tomorrow morning at eight o'clock there will be a meeting on Sixth Avenue at the entrance to Central Park. Be at that meeting with thousands of your fellow workers! Strike every shop and factory! And come ready to show the warmongers and nigger lovers that free white Americans can't be treated like the serfs of a foreign despot! Show them you can strike a blow for liberty!"

With this, Andrews moved toward the door. Every pair of eyes watched him. "I'll be there, lads. I promise you that. And I swear, by God, there'll be no draft tomorrow in this city, or John Andrews won't live to see the sun go down," he cried.

He turned on his heel and marched out the open door. The excited voices of the men drifted after him. Andrews walked to the corner briskly, ducked into an alleyway, and waited. In a few minutes the buck-toothed veteran and the small man who had started the questioning, joined him.

The former soldier grinned crookedly at Andrews. "They went for it, John. Oh, they're primed. You were great."

"So were you, Bert," Andrews said. He glanced at the small man. "You too, Ned."

Ned jerked his thumb at the grinning soldier. "This bastard really believes he's a goddamn hero, don't he? Some hero. Where's your medal, Billy Yank?"

"They don't give any for deserting," Bert said, showing his gums in a widening smile.

"Someday, Bert, an honest-to-goodness soldier is goin' to call you on that crap about being wounded, and you'll be choking on your damned buck teeth," Ned said.

"What are you sore about?" Bert asked, defensively. "You scared?"

Ned looked at him with disgust. "No, goddamn your lying eyes. But remember—I was at Antietam. I saw fine men dropping like cow turds—and I don't like you mocking 'em, that's all."

Andrews stepped between the two men. "Now, that's enough, lads. We've still got lots to do tonight. Lane's men are all set. Lane himself got into town a couple of hours ago," he said.

"Are you sure, John?" Bert asked.

"I talked to him, earlier. He's meeting with his group leaders at the warehouse."

"Then it's goin' to break tomorrow?" Bert asked. His face had turned pale and he licked his lips.

"Oh, for Christ sake, John—look at the hero! He'll beshit himself in a minute," Ned said scornfully.

"Are you losing your nerve, Bert?" Andrews asked coldly.

"No—— Hell, I was just askin', that's all." The ex-soldier looked from one to the other, his eyes sick with fear.

"It'll break tomorrow," Andrews said. "And what a day it's going to be! Now, come on, we've still got to cover the rest of the saloons on this street."

The three men walked off together to sow their seeds of hatred.

The ancient warehouse was a rotting wooden structure abutting an unused pier that jutted into the East River at the foot of 4th Street. The weather-beaten walls were scabrous with clinging flakes of peeling paint. Holes gaped in the roof and broken timbers poked up like splintery fingers.

The windows of the warehouse had been broken for years, but jagged pieces of glass were still fixed in the corners of the frames. The staircase to the main entrance was frail and shaky. Its banister was gone, taken long since for firewood by squatters who lived in shanties along the riverbank nearby. The door hung askew on broken hinges.

Inside, the place was a dank cavern. The floor planks creaked and yielded under a man's weight. In some parts, sections of the flooring had collapsed and musty odors crept up from the damp basement. Water dripped from rusted and corroded pipes, forming stagnant pools in hollows of the floor.

At one end of the long warehouse, a bull's-eye lantern threw a shaft of light. Just beyond the rim of illumination, a group of men stood shadowed and shapeless in the gloom. They listened raptly to a tall man whose sallow mustached face seemed cadaverous in the lantern light. He spoke in a voice thick with the creamy accent of Virginia.

"There's little for me to tell you lads. You know why you're here. You have your instructions. Any questions?" he asked.

"Cap'n Lane, do we get the inflammables now or wait until tomorrow," a voice drawled.

"Gordon will issue Greek fire to incendiary unit squad leaders at once."

"Yes suh."

"Any further questions?" Lane asked, peering into the darkness, trying to see the men's faces, wondering how they were taking this grim and unusual assignment.

There were no more questions. "All right, then. Incendiary squad leaders, draw your Greek fire. The rest, file out and rejoin your units. Good luck, men," Lane said.

The men filed past him, silently. Twenty picked lads. Each commanding ten volunteers who had filtered into the city during the past fortnight. They had remained in hiding with sympathizers in Staten Island farmhouses, in brownstones, in shacks and tenements.

Some had come to the city by way of Canada, others had been smuggled in on merchant ships. A few had arrived by train, by wagon, even on foot, assuming various disguises and identities. Now the time for concealment was ending. The waiting was over. Arms caches were dragged from secret storerooms. By morning, two hundred well-armed dedicated men would be on the move, following a master plan to burn ships at their moorings, important buildings and other objectives. During the confusion of an apparently spontaneous mass uprising against the draft, certain of these infiltrators had been selected to kill or capture the leading officials of the city and other prominent men, and to take power in New York.

The last man hurried down the rickety stairway. A few carried carpetbags which held jars of liquid Greek fire that had been handed to them by a young man. After they had gone, he called out softly, "That's it, Cap'n Lane."

"All right, Gordon."

"We've done all we can. The rest depends on what happens tomorrow. Damn it, Ross, I can't bring myself to trust the Yankee politicians in spite of all they've said about being on our side."

"We've got no choice but to string along with them."

Gordon sighed. "You think it'll work out, Ross?"

Lane shook his head. "I don't know. If we'd have won at Gettysburg last week we'd be certain of success. Still, the odds are with us. They've only got a little militia in the city and we won't have to worry ourselves too much about the police."

"I reckon we can handle a few cops."

"And we've got surprise on our side. They don't expect any trouble since it went so quietly yesterday."

"Hell, Ross, I don't want to be a calamity howler, but what if the Yankee politicians and the Copperheads don't back it up all the way, and the rising fizzles?"

Lane grinned, his teeth flashing in the lantern's beam. "Man can't expect to live forever, can he?"

Gordon laughed. "Figured that's what you'd say." He stooped and picked up the bull's-eye lantern. After a last look around, the men left and the warehouse was silent except for the drip, drip, drip from the leaking pipes.

A DROWSY Sunday night calm enveloped the Central Department Headquarters building of the Metropolitan Police, located at 300 Mulberry Street, at the corner of Bleecker. The handsome, two-year-old white stone structure usually bustled with activity, the telegraph keys chattering on long rows of tables where busy operators sent and received messages from the thirty-two precinct houses of the 2,000-man police force, squads of police leaving or entering the building, the sound of voices in the long corridors and in the huge high-windowed main room on the ground floor. In contrast, the headquarters was blanketed in soothing silence on this quiet night.

The building was the pride of the Metropolitan Police. Equipped with a modern heating system, it boasted of all the latest conveniences. No police department in the United States, perhaps in the world, had a more complete telegraphic system than did the Metropolitan Police. It was operated by the Telegraphic Bureau which occupied the spacious basement of the building.

James Crowley, the Bureau Supervisor, was a hard worker who demanded perfection from his linemen and telegraphers. The complex of telegraph lines was carried on poles which supported wires interconnecting each police precinct with the Central Office and with each other. In addition, long distance lines hooked up to relay stations and could be connected anywhere within the United States for the swift transmission of messages.

The telegraphic center in Police Headquarters was the vortex of a communications system in which the intricately crisscrossed wires strung on the poles along Third Avenue were vital arteries. This was the heart of the system, and its great weakness. Any serious damage to these lines could cripple whole sections of the network and without its telegraph in full operation the police would be severely hampered.

On the upper floors of the building, which were reached by a splendid mahogany stairway, were the offices of the three police commissioners—Thomas C. Acton, John Bergen, and James Bowen, at present away on active duty with the army as a Brigadier General of Volunteers. His duties devolved upon Acton and Bergen, a pair of efficient and highly competent officials.

The actual head of the department was Superintendent John Kennedy who was assisted in his work by four inspectors—Daniel Carpenter, James Leonard, George Dilks, and John Folk, commander of the Brooklyn police under Commissioner Bergen. Each of these men had his own office, as did the Chief of Detectives, Sergeant John Young.

Sixteen hand-picked men made up the Detective Bureau which Young commanded. He was a conscientious officer and even at this hour was still at his desk, studying reports from his men who were scattered at various points throughout the city. A hissing gas fixture cast a pale, yellowish glow in his small office. The clatter of wheels bumping over cobblestones came through the open window. Occasionally, there was the clip-clop of a trotting horse as a rider hurried down the street. The faint sound of many vehicles in steadily flowing traffic drifted in from nearby Broadway. A voice raised in argument and the tuneless whistling of a nighttime stroller floated up.

To Young, the reports which had been coming in were ominous, but no one else seemed concerned over them. For the twentieth time, he reread Detective Dusenberry's hastily scrawled note, which had been delivered to Young by a paid police informer. The message read:

Sergeant Young: A man named John Andrews is stirring the people to action against the draft and the colored. He is making treasonable speeches about the 10th Ward and especially along Allen Street. I am sticking to him. Dusenberry.

Young had brought the note to Superintendent Kennedy, but the Superintendent's reaction had dismayed him. Kennedy had merely shrugged his shoulders and said, "Let the blasted fool shoot his mouth off. He doesn't matter at all."

"But, sir—Andrews is a troublemaker. Let me give Dusenberry authority to arrest him."

Kennedy frowned at Young. "The man's got a right to talk. He's committing no crime," he said peevishly.

"When he spouts sedition, he is."

"We're policemen, not the Secret Service. If we arrested everyone who spoke against the draft, or the war, or Mr. Lincoln, we'd need a jailhouse bigger than Central Park to hold them all."

"I have other reports from my men, Superintendent. Everyone believes we're in for trouble tomorrow."

"You mean that meeting on Sixth Avenue? It will amount to nothing. Your lads claimed there was going to be an attack on the Arsenal yesterday and nothing came of it. Listen, Young— I've been a police officer a good many years—and I know the people of the city. And I know the scum that's doing all the swashbuckling. Rum pots and beer swillers. Gutter trash. They'll wake up tomorrow with big heads and forget all about mass meetings and starting trouble. Besides, we'll have men on hand at the Arsenal and the Provost Marshal's office. I'm going home, now—and I suggest you do the same, Young."

The interview was ended. The sallow-faced sixty-five-year-old Superintendent left, jauntily twirling the light Malacca cane he always carried.

That had been Sergeant Young's first rebuff of the evening. The second had come a while after Kennedy's departure. Another report was relayed to Young—this one from Detective John McCord. It had been sent from a drinking dive on Baxter Street which was a notorious hangout for Five Points roughs. The report mentioned that several Negroes had been badly beaten by gangsters, who had loudly declared, according to McCord:

"Wait until tomorrow. We'll decorate every lamp post in the city with a nigger. . . ."

This threat of violence was borne out when another detective sent word that several Negro shacks at the foot of Carmine Street had been set afire by a band of drunken men. At this news, Young had decided that the Mayor must be advised of the situation.

Alone, now, in his office, despite the tranquillity about him, Young could not dispel a foreboding of evil. The detective stirred uneasily in his chair. He wished he could agree with the Mayor and with Kennedy that what he regarded as menacing portents were only figments of his own anxieties. But Young knew the city and the volatile nature of it. He sensed the unrest stirring in the narrow streets and twisting alleys of the slums.

He sat quietly for a long time. At last he rose from his chair and walked out of the office. His footsteps echoed hollowly on the oak-planked floor as he went down the long corridor. Young had decided to see for himself the temper of the city. He strolled over to Broadway. The night was hot, but Broadway was crowded. He headed downtown, past the St. Nicholas Hotel and the Metropolitan. He paused to look into the attractive window display at Lord and Taylor's, a bit farther south at Grand Street.

Gradually, his feelings of apprehension dissolved. The handsomely attired crowds, the carriages and hacks filled with pleasure seekers, the well-stocked stores and busy restaurants banished his dark thoughts. Surely, nothing could upset the solidity of New York. Nothing could disturb this city where merchant princes reigned, and which everyone hailed as the greatest metropolis in the world. This summer's night was not for worrying. The city was safe.

Young decided that what he needed was an order of butter cakes and coffee before his trek home to Harlem. He noticed a coffee saloon close to Barnum's Museum and went into the place. Soon he was contentedly sipping coffee and eating tasty hot cakes dripping with butter. But, suddenly, like a warning, there was a momentary grumble of thunder and a flash of lightning that lit the sky with an eerie glow.

ERUPTION

Monday, July 13—Wednesday, July 15, 1863

. . . *1*

THE city grudgingly stirred awake as the first pallid streaks lightened the slate sky. No freshening breeze sprang up to soften the unrelenting heat and in the uptown rural areas herds of cattle huddled close in pastures and meadows where dew covered the grass and stubborn night mists clung in hollows. Even at the day's earliest hour, the temperature was uncomfortably hot.

Milkmen's carts appeared on the streets, cans clanging and metal rimmed wheels grinding over cobblestones. Men with sleep-dulled eyes forced themselves into weary wakefulness for the day's work.

Along the docks where tall ships swayed at their moorings, pier bosses marked cargoes for loading or unloading and made ready for the customary shape-up of the longshoremen.

Docile truck horses clomped from their stalls and were hitched to vans by bearded drivers, who sulkily tightened cinches and straps, wiping big, calloused hands on leathern aprons, their faces stony with inner anger. They felt themselves trapped by endless work, by families in crowded living quarters, and now by the draft, an ugly threat to the little security their jobs offered.

In the cattle pens adjoining the Bull's Head Tavern at 44th Street and Lexington Avenue, herdsmen nudged the cattle into corrals. White-smocked butchers, sipping coffee from thick mugs, eyed the stock shrewdly and calculated opening bidding prices when the market sales began. The cattle lowed in doleful chorus as if the beasts were aware that beyond the corrals were the ramps leading up to the slaughterhouse where keen knives were waiting.

The cars started rolling downtown from Yorkville and Harlem, crowded with workingmen who clutched lunch pails and jostled mercilessly to grab a seat on an outbound car. Wheels screeched on rails as the drivers flicked their whips across the backs of the powerful horses.

Newsboys jockeyed for spots at ferry depots where the boats from Brooklyn and Jersey docked every few minutes, disgorging loads of work-bound passengers.

"*News! Times! Tribune! Herald!* Latest from General Meade! Latest from General Grant! Latest about the Draft! Latest from Europe!" the vendors shouted.

The masses streaming down the ferry gangplanks were a cross section of the more than 800,000 who lived in and near New York City. There were factory workers in rough clothes—dull-eyed, stoop-shouldered men and young, grimy boys, and clerks who lived in the suburbs of New Jersey or the reaches of Brooklyn, disdainfully superior in their neat suits and starched shirts.

The roadways were suddenly flooded with an onrush of traffic. Every kind of commercial vehicle jammed the inadequate streets. Huge drays, hauled by teams of fours locked hub to hub, the drivers jeering and cursing at each other as they sawed on reins, backing and filling to get free. Porters pushed heavily laden two-wheeled handcarts, threading by the steaming flanks of sweating horses. Even at this early hour, an ice vendor trundled his wagon through the busy streets crying, "Oh, Ice! Oh,

Ice! Oh, Rockland Lake Water Ice!" Sweet-potato sellers with little wheeled stoves roasted yams on glowing charcoals. There were hawkers urging the passers-by to purchase an astonishing variety of objects, each adding his special cry to the din.

Somehow, the entangled traffic managed to unsnarl itself and rolled slowly, but without interruption. Pedestrians dashed heedlessly across the streets, disregarding the vehicles and miraculously managing to escape being trampled to death by the horses.

And the city roared to the height of its wakefulness.

. . . **2**

ORMALLY, before 7:00 A.M. every dock on the Hudson River front where the ocean-going ships tied up, and all the piers along the East River, were crowded with groups of men waiting for a day's work as stevedores.

The pier bosses, thick-necked, arrogant men who had the temperament of brutal plantation overseers, took their pick of the eager men hungry for work. If a man displeased the boss, he was warned never to show up at that pier again. Since the bosses were feared and notorious roughs, few dared disobey them. They usually had criminal records; many had been in prison for felonies ranging from rape to murder. They were hired by the contractors who held a monopoly on the handling of ocean-going freightage. In recent years, the water front had been the scene of fierce battles between rival gangs whose leaders sought to get the rich longshore contracts. The victors not only broke more heads than their rivals, but also handed out huge sums in bribes—even the lowliest hack politician, no matter how vaguely connected with the award of dock contracts, got his cut of graft.

Whoever held power, both Negro and white stevedores fared badly. During June, white stevedores along the West side banded together and went out on strike. They demanded twenty-five cents an hour during the regular nine-hour day and fifty cents after 9:00 P.M. The stoppage was squelched when the pier bosses hired hundreds of work-starved Negroes to move the cargoes. Tensions ran high on the water front. Five hundred police guarded the docks, and sea-borne army supplies were handled by military prisoners from Fort Lafayette and Governor's Island.

The bosses planted stool pigeons among the strikers to find out who had organized the strike, and the men responsible were thoroughly beaten and then black-listed. Other provocateurs stirred the gullible strikers against the Negroes. These agents did their work well. The white longshoremen ambushed the Negroes, and a near race war broke out on the docks. A fire, set by incendiaries, destroyed a quantity of goods on one dock. This loss gave the bosses an excuse for a general wage cut against the Negro strikebreakers. When they protested, the pier bosses told them, "It's too damn dangerous to employ you niggers— so you've got to share our losses."

When the violence grew out of hand, the contractors settled with the strikers, who were in no position to hold prolonged bargaining sessions after a week or so without work. They had to accept the first offer of two dollars for the basic day, and twenty-five cents an hour overtime after 6:00 P.M. The dockers returned to work, and the Negroes were once again relegated to employment in swill milk distilleries and the cleaning of hog and cattle pens. Most of them were left without any employment. But the shrewd pier bosses kept a percentage of dockside jobs open to them. They were a constant reminder to the whites that any new strike action would be broken by the mass hiring of Negroes.

On Monday, July 13, it was not strange that the pier bosses were the first to sense that something out of the ordinary was about to happen in the city. Only a few men showed up for the shape-up hour. There were more Negroes than whites waiting to be hired. At first, the bosses thought it was another strike—but there had been no warning of this from the informers on the payroll. The bosses chewed their cigars and sent emissaries out to nearby saloons to garner some hint of what was going on.

They found out soon enough. About 7:15 A.M. large gangs armed with crowbars, baling hooks and clubs showed up on the water front. Individual groups merged to form unruly mobs. Nobody knew where they had gathered or who had sent them. Self-appointed delegates from the mobs on both the East and West sides of town entered machine shops, foundries and factories on the river fronts. Incoming workers were prevented from reporting for work and forced into the mobs' ranks.

The marchers held placards bearing the words "NO DRAFT" in crude lettering. At each pier men broke out of the mass and attacked the waiting Negro longshoremen. The alarm was spread by Negro cartmen who lashed their horses into frantic speed and dashed uptown giving the warning of what was coming. The Negro stevedores fled. They vanished into the crooked streets and nameless alleys that ran into a maze of courts and littered, weed-choked backyards.

The white longshoremen who had reported for the shape-up gladly joined the mob. Pier bosses tried to frighten some into working with the threat of future black-listing. But the newly found unity made the men feel strong. They were masters of the water front on this day. Where the pier bosses grew too troublesome, direct action was taken. At Pier 9, North River, longshoremen dumped the boss and his henchmen into the water. This was the underdog's day on the docks.

But the mob had no time to waste gloating over petty triumphs. Earnest looking workers among them kept the march progressing uptown. Voices called, "On to the meeting! On to Central Park!"

As the throng surged northward, leaders emerged to guide it toward Sixth Avenue, through the side streets, and soon units of the separate groups from both water fronts came together. All the way uptown delegations went into industrial places, forcing employers to close shop and workers to join the demonstration.

On Sixth, Eighth and Ninth Avenues the street railway car drivers left their posts and marched along. Passengers in working clothes were recruited. Public transportation came to a halt on the West side, but private vehicles were not molested.

Once the demonstration had channeled itself into the main thoroughfare which led to its destination—a rock-strewn, open lot adjoining Central Park—hundreds of spectators lined Sixth Avenue to watch the motley procession. The marchers were boisterous but made no attempt to harm either onlookers or property. While many in the noisy crowd were sincerely opposed to the draft, some regarded it as a lark. A number of women were in the line of march. They were the loudest and most vehement in denouncing the draft.

No accurate count could be made of the crowd but conservative estimates placed it at around 10,000. One viewer, the son of Charles King, President of Columbia College, noted that, "It took a full twenty minutes for the mob to pass a given point and the paraders filled the roadway from curb to curb."

Occasionally, a policeman on his rounds found himself the object of hooting and catcalling but the demonstration, in the main, seemed more festive than menacing. At last people began filling the lot where the meeting was to be held. Makeshift platforms had been erected. As the crowd poured in, speakers started haranguing it. One after another, skilled rabble rousers whipped up the audience with inflammatory speeches. With each speech, the crowd's temper grew steadily more threatening.

The great throng listened and shouted its approval. Speakers who were recognized by sight or name received earsplitting ovations. The men who addressed the gathering were Democratic politicians, local office holders, and editors of antiadministration papers. A rumor had been circulated that both Fernando and Ben Wood were going to speak, but neither one appeared, although those far back in the crowd raised cheers for the Woods every time a new speaker climbed to the platform.

Finally John Andrews jumped up and sparked off the mob. He spoke emotionally, dramatically. "Men! Free Americans! Why are we standing here? The time for speeches has passed! The moment for action has arrived! Free Americans! Stop the draft! On to Marshal Jenkins' office! Smash the draft!"

Ross Lane, clad in workingman's clothes, leaped up alongside of Andrews. "On to the Marshal's office!" he cried. It was taken up and repeated by thousands who chanted the words like a war cry. Men began moving off downtown, shouting and beckoning to others. An eddying movement passed through the crowd, then a mighty surge as the mob pressed forward together.

Lane grinned at Andrews. "It's starting, John," he said.

"Yes. Are your men ready?" Andrews asked with a hint of tightness in his voice.

"You know they are. We'll cut the telegraph wires as we hit Third Avenue. Don't worry about us. Make certain your people deliver all they promised."

"This is the day we've been waiting for—all of us. Our people will rise to the occasion," Andrews said pompously.

"Talk is easy, John. Frankly, I think all you Copperheads are tin horns."

"Wait a minute. Do you include me in that opinion?"

Lane eyed Andrews appraisingly. "No. I don't think so. But after all, you're not a Yankee. You're a Virginian. We'll find out soon enough, though, whether you're men—or windbags."

"I don't much care for your attitude," Andrews said.

"I'll apologize if I'm wrong. I think you'd better go along with the crowd and keep them stirred up."

"I know what has to be done," Andrews said brusquely.

The men jumped from the platform. The mob was pushing out of the lot, stragglers hurrying after the main body. Off to one side stood a group of ten men dressed as laborers. Lane gestured toward them. "My men are waiting. Good luck, Andrews."

"Good luck, Captain."

Lane walked to his group. They huddled around him. He issued last minute instructions and then, stepping away from them, whistled shrilly between his fingers three times. A cart driver who had been drowsing in the sun snapped up at the signal. He touched his horse with the whip and drew the van up to the men. In a second, the tailboard was down. One man jumped up into the wagon and began passing long-handled axes to the others. When the last ax had been handed out, Lane waved to the driver who lashed his horse and drove away, rounding a corner and dashing out of sight.

Each man shouldered his ax and fell in behind Lane. The small band marched out into the path of the mob. They had marched this way at Savage Station, Antietam, Chancellorsville, and only the week before, at Gettysburg. To them this city and these streets were merely the terrain of another battlefield.

This was to be a unique battle—one fought without skirmishers and artillery. No regimental flags whipped in the van and no bugles sounded. It was to be a battle of craftiness and cunning. But these men were soldiers and asked no questions. They had volunteered for a mission and if it called upon them to wear laborer's clothes and carry axes they would do what was required of them. They were soldiers and they marched with the easy, loping stride of combat veterans.

. . . **3**

THE Black Joke crew gathered early at Marshal Jenkins' office. The men wore their volunteer fire department uniforms—red shirt, wide belt with an ornate buckle, and black pants tucked into boot tops. These belts of shiny leather had a less prosaic use than simply holding up the wearer's trousers, which were, in fact, supported by wide white suspenders. The belts, when wrapped around a man's knuckles with the buckle outward, made a dreadful weapon. The firemen would sail into a fray twirling their belts, slashing with the buckle. They swaggered arrogantly outside the Marshal's office now, winding the belts around their fists, taunting the policemen who guarded the place, and boasting loudly about their intentions.

The police paid no attention to the threats of the firemen. They were old antagonists and had clashed many times in free-for-all brawls. While the volunteers grew more pugnacious, the mob heading downtown turned vicious. Marchers raided saloons and liquor stores along the route. Rocks crashed into plate glass windows and the streets became littered with broken glass. Everyone seemed to have a bottle and all semblance of discipline vanished.

The great crowd funneled down into 46th Street. A few police tried to turn it back but the oncoming mass simply rode over the officers. As the mob poured into Third Avenue and blocked all traffic, Ross Lane gave his men a command. They shinnied up the telegraph poles and slashed the wires with their axes.

Demonstrators climbed onto the roofs of halted streetcars, jumped up and down, and whooped senselessly. Grogshops were looted and the saloon next to the Provost Marshal's office was practically demolished as hundreds scrambled to get inside. Chairs, tables, glasses and mirrors were shattered. A wild fracas broke out to complete the wreckage of the place.

Captain Galen Porter, commanding the sixty-man police detail at the draft office, was an experienced officer. He knew his men could handle the Black Joke—but not this howling mob. Porter ordered the men inside the building for their protection. The door was opened wide enough to permit one policeman at a time to slip in, and the crowd began to jeer.

No vehicle moved along Third Avenue. The streetcars were halted in a line that stretched north to the terminus at 130th Street and south along the avenue to Cooper Union, and down the Bowery to Park Row. Anxious passengers far from the disturbance poked their heads from the windows to see what was wrong. People gathered on rooftops to look down at the blocked traffic and tried to guess the reasons for the tie-up.

A rumor flashed through the mob at the Marshal's office that the draft had been canceled. This started exultant demonstrations. Staggering men, waving half-empty whisky bottles, jigged in the street. They cheered and pounded one another on the back. No one doubted the report and it seemed to have a good basis since the 9:00 A.M. deadline for starting the drafting had passed without any indication that the office was opening. Shouts of "We licked the nigger lovers!" were heard on all sides. Less enthusiastic demonstrators began to drift away. Most remained to celebrate and make a holiday of their victory.

Captain Porter conferred with Marshal Jenkins inside the building. No word from higher authority had come to suspend the draft and Jenkins refused to do so without orders. "Far as

I'm concerned, it's on. I'll delay until ten-thirty and not a minute later," he told the police officer.

"That mob is mean," Porter said.

"No rabble will stop me from carrying out my duty. You're supposed to keep order, Captain Porter. I expect you to do your job as I'll do mine."

"Very well, Marshal. I'd better send for reinforcements. I'd telegraph the Central Office from the 19th Precinct but those devils have cut the wires. One of your clerks can get through to headquarters in civilian clothes but none of my men would stand a chance."

Jenkins beckoned to a young clerk who listened gravely to Porter's instructions. He slipped out the back way and mingled with the mob for several blocks, then hurried to Mulberry Street.

The crowd's exultation slackened as new rumors spread that not only was the draft still in force but the quota had been trebled as punishment for the demonstration. Talk flew back and forth and within the mob brawls flared up. The Black Joke men became embroiled with a rival engine company and the volunteers went at each other, fists and belts swinging. Kegs of beer were dragged from the wreckage of the saloon and set up on the sidewalk to be emptied in minutes as greedy drinkers scooped up the brew in cupped hands or simply plunged their faces into the foamy liquid and guzzled their fill.

Lane's men stood hunched together, indolently leaning on their axes, taking no part in the disorderly goings on. They chewed tobacco and spat streams of brown juice while awaiting further orders with a patience and impassivity that could only be learned on the battlefield. A few paces from them, Lane waited, too. The fate of the whole plan hinged on what would happen next, he thought. If the crowd continued behaving as it was, wasting time and energy in rioting and violence, there was little hope of success.

Everything depended on insurrectionary thousands, properly

controlled and led, ready to dare open rebellion. But this yowling mass was merely a drunken rabble which would eventually break up unless something drastic happened. With each moment, opportunity was slipping away.

The wires were down and most police stations were out of touch with the Central Office. But some long distance lines were still in operation. Help could be summoned from outside the city. Now was the time to strike. Yet, while the Marshal's office stayed closed and no names were drawn for the draft there was nothing to impel action from the mob.

However, Marshal Jenkins was a man of his word. At 10:30 he signaled a clerk to raise the window blinds, an indication the office was ready for business. As the shades went up, an angry yell came from the mob.

"They're starting the draft!" men cried.

Led by the Black Joke crew, hundreds dashed for the building. The windows crashed in and the doors were battered down as a shouting horde rushed into the office. A double line of husky policemen managed to halt the invaders at the wooden railing. The firemen tightened the belts around their fists. Men brandished clubs and iron bars. A loud voice cried out above the uproar, "Spin that damn wheel and you're dead men!"

Standing at the table beside the draft wheel, Marshal Jenkins faced the hostile crowd. He met their smoldering gaze with icy calmness. A cluster of pale, white-lipped clerks bunched behind him. Jenkins cleared his throat and began to speak. His words were drowned in the clamor of the onlookers. Jenkins said, "In accordance with the National Conscription Law enacted March 3, 1863, I hereby state that the draft for this Ninth Enrollment District, Twenty-first Ward, New York City, shall now commence as prescribed by regulations."

"You bastard, you'll look fine at the end of a rope!" a man shouted.

Jenkins deliberately turned his back on the crowd. He nodded to Southwick, his chief clerk, who blindfolded Carpenter again amid a growing din. Southwick then turned the wheel crank and the drum began to spin. As it revolved, a terrible, hate-filled cry went up both inside and outside the building. Word went out to the jostling thousands in the street that the drawing had started. In the office a wild voice roared, "Brothers! Don't let the murdering sons of bitches get away with this!"

A whisky bottle whizzed by Jenkins' head and crashed against the wall. A Black Joke fireman struck a policeman; the officer cracked the fireman's skull with a blow from his locust stick. In the street, someone fired a revolver. The shot hit a streetcar horse and the wounded animal collapsed to the cobblestones, neighing and thrashing about. A piece of paving block sailed into the building through the broken window.

Captain Porter shouted, "Clear the room! Clear the room!" He led the charge, his stick thudding on heads and shoulders. In seconds, there was a tangled scramble. Some of the police, close on Porter's heels, slugged their way into the street, only to be swallowed by the mob.

"Out the rear door!" Marshal Jenkins shouted. He snatched up a portfolio containing the names of the drafted men and all the enrollment lists. With his clerks following, the Marshal dashed through the back entrance. The few policemen left in the room also fled. Now the rioters were in full possession of the detested place. A man jumped onto the table and attacked the draft wheel with a crowbar. Several powerful blows smashed it open and the slips of paper fluttered out like large snowflakes.

Men gleefully splintered the desks and chairs. Every window was broken. More people pressed inside. A man pulled a liquid filled jar from his pocket. Shouting a warning, he hurled it against the wall. The jar exploded with a small bang. A noxious sulphur odor arose and flames danced in the flowing liquid.

"That's Greek fire! Let's get the hell out of here," someone yelled.

"My God, we'll be burned alive!" a woman shrieked. She turned to run, stumbled, and was knocked down by the mad rush for the door. Heedlessly, the crowd trampled her to death. The rioters fought to reach the exit. The flickering flames caught hold and spread rapidly. Soon, the whole room was engulfed in fire.

Outside, individual policemen were surrounded by kicking, punching men. Captain Porter, bleeding from innumerable scratches, his uniform ripped, led a dozen officers who had managed to keep together in a group. They fought effectively. Locust sticks took a toll. More rioters joined the fray. Porter's club was wrenched from his hand. In desperation, he drew his pistol and fired from the hip into the crowd. The other policemen started shooting, too. Suddenly, a path was cleared for them. They fled toward Lexington Avenue and the rioters pursued them across the lots. The police fired at their tormentors, who fell back and contented themselves with hurling rocks at the escaping policemen.

Three men sprawled dead from police bullets and a woman lay dying with a stomach wound. The sight of the dead men and the agonized woman infuriated the mob. The rioters dashed about screaming with inarticulate rage.

They overturned and burned streetcars and sacked every store in the neighborhood. Meanwhile, fire gutted Marshal Jenkins' office and spread through the partition walls to the lager beer saloon and Pettigrew's carriage factory. The upper floors blazed and fire darted from the tenement windows.

Residents fled the building and only a few managed to save anything as the fire spread rapidly. One weeping woman, three small children clutching at her skirts, stood on the sidewalk by a pitiful pile of poor household belongings. Her home was gone and all her possessions destroyed. She wept over this senseless destruction, the more because she had been the victim of people with whom she sympathized. She hated the draft, too—and with

good reason. Her husband had been taken on Saturday, in the
first call. . . .

Even before Captain Porter's messenger reached Police Headquarters, word of the outbreak had been flashed there over the
telegraph. Lane's men had done their sabotage well enough, but
no one could have forseen that James Crowley, Police Telegraphic Bureau Chief, would be riding to work in civilian clothes
on a Third Avenue car which was stopped by the mob. The car
in which Crowley was a passenger came to a halt only a block
from the Marshal's office. He had seen the wires cut. He left the
car, and with the mob boiling about him, calmly started splicing
the severed lines together. He was immediately surrounded by
a crowd of drunken men.

"What are you doin' with them wires?" a hulking giant demanded.

"Just getting them out of the way, lads," Crowley said, smiling
cheerfully. "We'll show the bastards they can't step on us, won't
we?"

"That's the spirit, bucko!" the big man cried, slapping Crowley
on the back with a great paw.

The police officer linked arms with him and said, "Come on—
let's serve the cause proper. We'll clear away the wires together."

The drunk stumbled along with Crowley. At each pole,
Crowley stopped long enough to connect the ends of dangling
wires and lash them into place. A few rioters who vaguely understood what he was doing tried to stop him but were chased off
by his new friend. Crowley knew the schematic plan of the
police telegraph system by memory. He reconnected most of
the lines linking the precincts with Mulberry Street. He had
almost finished this work when he was recognized by one of the
rioters who raised a hue and cry.

Crowley fled toward the nearest station house, the 19th Precinct on East 59th Street, with the rioters after him. He shook

them off by ducking through alleys, scaling back fences, and finally losing them in the welter of rubble-littered yards. Luckily, not one of those who had pursued him was sober enough to remember what had started the whole affair. An unscathed liquor store offered them fresh loot and they were soon fighting each other for it. Crowley's repairs were left intact.

At the 19th Precinct, Crowley found only a doorman on duty. The officers were either out on rounds or had been assigned to guard the Marshal's office. Crowley sent an urgent telegram to Headquarters:

19th Precinct to Central Office. 9:15 A.M.
Laborers have suspended work and are gathering with crowbars and other weapons for grand demonstration at 677 Third Avenue. Trouble brewing. Telegraph lines cut. Rush large force.

Crowley.

. . . *4*

A SHORT while earlier, Police Superintendent John Kennedy had decided to observe the situation at the draft offices in person. Detectives had been sending in reports all morning about disorders along the water front and workers' demonstrations against the draft. Still Kennedy refused to admit the threat of real trouble. Intransigence was Kennedy's great fault as a police officer. He was convinced that his Metropolitans could handle any situation and did not believe there would be a mass attack on the Arsenal, where a strong police detail and a bat-

tery of militia artillery were posted. He did, however, take a
precautionary step and sent a telegram alerting all precincts:

From Central Office: 9:00 A.M.

To all stations in New York and Brooklyn: Recall your reserves.
Platoon and hold them at the station houses subject to further orders.

John A. Kennedy, Superintendent

After sending this wire, Kennedy had climbed into his surrey
and gone off on his inspection tour unarmed except for a light
cane. It was typical of him not to notify anyone in the building
that he was leaving or to disclose his intentions.

The Superintendent was a thin, wiry, sallow-complexioned
man who regarded other high ranking police officials, particularly the Commissioners, with disdain, because they were political appointees. He had come up from the ranks, reaching his
present five-thousand-dollar-a-year post after long service as a
policeman. He had started on the old Municipal force at an
annual salary of eight hundred dollars.

He had a polite relationship with Commissioners Acton and
Bergen and was entirely neutral in their continuing struggle with
Governor Seymour who was trying to remove the Republican
commissioners and replace them with Democrats.

This anomalous situation was an outgrowth of the Metropolitan Police Act passed in 1857. It had established the present
organization. The law provided that the Governor appoint a
Board of Commissioners to preside over the Metropolitan Police. This had become necessary because of the scandalous
abuses during the mayoralty of Fernando Wood who had created the first uniformed force—the Municipal Police—and had
run it with a shocking incidence of corruption and graft.

The condition grew so shameful that the State government
stepped in and formed the Metropolitan Police. Wood refused
to disband the Municipals and as a result, the city had two
police departments. Finally, in July, 1857, the Municipals and

the Metropolitans fought an open battle in the streets while the criminal element looked on with glee. Troops finally restored order, and court action forced the disbandment of the Municipals. Control of the police now rested with the state and not the city officials.

As one of his last official acts, Republican Governor Edward Morgan, who had preceded Seymour in Albany, appointed Acton, Bowen, and Bergen for five-year terms. Governor Seymour did not relish the idea of allowing a politically hostile Police Board to remain in office. For months, he had attempted one legal move after another to unseat the three men. All his efforts failed and the feud continued. It did not effect the efficiency of the Metropolitan Police because the Commissioners were responsible and devoted men dedicated to running an effective police department.

Like most professionals, Kennedy had benign contempt for amateurs and the Commissioners fell into that category. The Board also included, as pro-tem members, the Mayors of New York and Brooklyn. The Superintendent had small regard for Opdyke and even less for Brooklyn's mayor, Martin Kalbfleisch. In his dealings with these men, Kennedy acted arbitrarily on matters concerning police work. His abrupt departure from Headquarters without notifying anyone was an example of his behavior.

Shortly after Kennedy had left, Crowley's telegram came over the wires and caused widespread consternation. A few minutes later, Captain Porter's disheveled messenger rushed into the building. He blurted out his story to the first officer he met, and since Kennedy could not be located, the man was rushed upstairs to see Acton.

Thomas Acton was a nervous man who burned with energy. The telegram had set him pacing the floor and the messenger's description of the mob was no nerve balm. While Acton had no prior police experience and knew nothing of how to suppress a mob, he was a top-notch executive, the owner of a successful brokerage house, highly intelligent, and with the ability to make positive decisions.

He recalled that a platoon of Invalid Corps troops had been assigned to special duty with the police and were still in their bivouac at the Park Barracks near City Hall. Rather than move police details with Kennedy absent, Acton decided to order the soldiers uptown as reinforcements for Porter's detail.

A mounted courier was soon galloping down Broadway with orders to the Officer of the Day at the Park Barracks. Shortly after his arrival, buglers blew "Assembly," drummers beat the long roll, and in ten minutes the veteran platoon was on the march up Park Row and into Third Avenue, carrying loaded Springfields with fixed bayonets at right shoulder shift and forty rounds of ball ammunition in their cartridge boxes.

In the meantime the mob was calling for John Andrews. He listened to their clamor for a few minutes. Then, boosted by willing hands, Andrews climbed atop a butcher's wooden shanty. He posed there, legs widespread, arms akimbo, a fine figure, and he stared out over the upturned faces of the crowd. As far as he could see along Third Avenue the street was solid with humanity and vehicles. People clung to the sides and roofs of streetcars, and for a distance of some blocks, heads were poked out of every dwelling window. Smoke from the unhampered fires rose in greasy black columns and spiraled over the mob. At intervals, a crashing beam sent up a geyser of sparks.

From his perch, Andrews could see beyond Third Avenue where new buildings were being constructed on the lots between Third and Lexington Avenues. The skeletal frames of the structures were covered with onlookers. People swarmed over piles of earth from basement excavations. Andrews felt this was an exalted hour comparable to Bunker Hill or the storming of the Bastille. He saw himself as a leader whose name would go down in history. When he raised his hands for silence those nearest him cried, "Shut up back there! Andrews is going to speak!"

Gradually the throng fell silent. The frantic clanging of a fire bell broke the sudden stillness. No one answered the alarm and in a few moments the bell stopped ringing. With the snapping flames as a background, Andrews started his speech. His strong voice carried almost to the outer fringes of the mob and even those who could barely hear him stayed quiet. The drunken disorder stopped briefly.

"Fellow free men and fellow citizens!" Andrews began, "for free men we still are. You have done nobly. You have struck a blow that will live forever in the annals of liberty. I've said you've done nobly, fellow citizens. But I tell you what I want you to do now, what you must do! You must organize, boys!"

A burst of applause resounded through the crowd. The speaker nodded to acknowledge the ovation. "Yes, organize, keep together, appoint leaders and smash this damned abolitionist draft into the dust!" he cried.

They cheered him and he basked in the sound. He smiled confidently, allowing the swelling approval to grow. Then, testing his power over them, he made the slightest gesture with his hand. The cheering was stilled at once. Andrews owned this crowd.

"Yes, that's what you must do, boys! Organize! And for the work ahead, we need weapons—plenty of them! Arms, friends, we need arms! A gun for every man!"

This evoked an outburst that made the previous demonstrations seem like whispers. Men threw their hats in the air, yelled and whistled between their fingers. Andrews stood waving and nodding. At last when enough quiet was restored for him to continue, he said, "If you can't find anyone with enough heart to lead you, by God, I'll lead you myself!" He lifted his arms over his head. "Now, lads—there's the Arsenal on Seventh Avenue filled with guns! Come on—follow me—on to the Arsenal!"

"To the Arsenal!" they repeated, over and over until it became a screaming chant.

The mob pressed back and forth with the lurching movements of a monstrous beast, its thousand arms waving in frenzied gestures. A man on horseback made his way through the mass. He stood up in the stirrups, hands cupped about his mouth crying, "Not the Arsenal, mates! There's soldiers with cannon on guard! Not the Arsenal!"

His words were greeted with a roar. People closed about him, grabbing the bridle, clinging to his stirrups. He shouted, "Soldiers coming up Third Avenue! We've got to stop them!"

"Don't worry, we'll take care of the bayonets!" the rioters called out to him.

At first, Andrews thought the rider was a police spy. But many in the crowd recognized him. He was a well-known leader in the section of First Avenue called "Mackerelville" and went by the name of "Big Tim." The nickname suited him for he was a giant in build and stature.

"Police Superintendent Kennedy's dead, boys!" he bellowed. "They killed him over on Lexington!"

"Serves the bastard right!" a man declared loudly.

"Let's get the nigger-loving bayonets! We'll show 'em whose city this is!" a man shouted.

"You do it!" Big Tim cried, digging his spurs into the horse's flanks and sending him off at a gallop through the mob, making people scatter in every direction.

Word of Superintendent Kennedy's fate swept through the crowd, but the rioters were far more interested in the news that soldiers were coming up Third Avenue. Some slipped quietly away. Others ran about shouting confused orders hoping that such frantic activity might conceal their fearful anxiety.

Still on the roof of the shed, Andrews felt his exhilaration draining away. He was empty and tired. A down gust drove

the smoke into the mob and Andrews saw the rioters as indistinct, shadowy figures. The shouts and the turbulence seemed
unreal. He stood there, presenting the façade of a leader, yet
struggling to hide rising fear.

. . . 5

T HE Superintendent of Police was not dead. Kennedy was
lying on the crude planking of a jouncing, lurching cartman's wagon which was racing downtown toward Police Headquarters.

A man named John Eagan clung to the side of the rocking cart
with one hand and tried to steady Kennedy's lanky body with
the other. The policeman's face was battered almost beyond
recognition. Bruises lumped his features. His iron-gray hair was
matted with blood. His clothing was torn. One sleeve had been
ripped from his jacket. Kennedy used all his self control to keep
from crying out with pain. Every jolt of the wagon sent hot
'knives through him. He touched his ribs gingerly and even that
slight pressure made him wince. He opened his eyes, swollen
into discolored slits, and looked at Eagan. He tried to speak, but
Eagan gently restrained him.

"Lie quietly, John. We'll soon be at Headquarters," Eagan
said.

Kennedy nodded. He shut his eyes and remembered the hate-
contorted faces that had surrounded him, and the awful moment when he knew he was trapped by the mob.

His ride uptown had been uneventful, through tranquil, fa-

miliar streets to Mannierre's office at 28th Street and Broadway
where a small orderly crowd listened placidly as names were
drawn from the wheel. Bored policemen stood by idly twirling
their sticks in lazy circles.

After chatting with Mannierre a while, Kennedy had climbed
into the surrey again and started for Jenkins' office. Turning
east, he drove along Lexington Avenue and soon noticed the
columns of smoke and the traffic stalled on Third Avenue. He
saw unruly groups running uptown and even from that distance
heard massed shouting. Then he saw men with assorted weapons
drinking whisky and realized these were the fringes of a dangerous mob. He whipped up his horse.

Everywhere, fire bells were tolling. At 44th Street he tried to
drive onto Third Avenue but by now thousands of yelling people blocked his passage. All types of vehicles had been abandoned in the street. He saw vivid splashes of red and orange in
the thick smoke that hung over the doomed buildings. Sick with
apprehension, he realized the blaze must be in the Marshal's
Office—and dreaded to think what must have happened to Captain Porter and his detail.

He found a hitching post and tied his horse to it, then hurried on foot toward Third Avenue, nervously swinging his
Malacca cane. He cut through an open lot and had gone only
a short distance when his path was blocked by a number of
men. Among them were several whom Kennedy had arrested in
the past.

One man pointed at him and shouted, "It's that son of a
bitch, Kennedy!" He reached out to grab the Superintendent
who stepped back and slashed him across the face with his cane.

"Out of my way, Dugan!" he cried.

A red welt formed on Dugan's cheek. Bellowing, he charged
Kennedy, his companions following. They knocked Kennedy
down, kicking and pummeling him. Scrambling to his feet, the
police officer broke free and ran blindly. Now, he was sur-

rounded by shrieking women who scratched and tore at him.
Somehow, he managed to keep running. He heard voices yelling, "It's Kennedy! Kill him! Kill him!"

The blows meant nothing. He neither felt nor minded them.
He stumbled and fell over an embankment close to one of the
new buildings and crashed headlong into a pool of stagnant
rain water. They leaped on top of him and pushed his face into
the stinking slime. He tore himself from them and scrabbled up
the slope. At the top, he fell again, gasping. As he struggled
to rise, he saw a well-dressed man running toward him. With
a last flicker of consciousness, he recognized the man and called
out to him, "John Eagan! Save me! In the name of the Blessed
Virgin! Save me!"

From far off, he faintly heard Eagan shout, "That's enough,
you damned fools! Let him be!"

The rioters obeyed John Eagan. The wealthy builder em-
ployed many of them and he had much influence in that neighborhood. They were afraid of him, too, for Eagan could kill a
man with one blow of his huge fists. Even at this moment the
incensed rioters dared not defy him. They stood by and watched
while Eagan commandeered a cartman and placed the unconscious Kennedy in the wagon. But those who had not seen the
cart bear Kennedy away, who only saw the attack, spread the
rumor that the police official had been killed.

The driver rolled to a stop outside the new headquarters
building. Acton was standing on the steps anxiously watching
for Kennedy. When the wagon pulled up, he glanced into it
and thought the bloodied man lying there was a drunk beaten
up in some barroom brawl. Then, he saw Eagan and said, in
surprised tones, "Who's this, Mr. Eagan? I'll have the driver
haul him around to the rear. The surgeon will patch him up
and he can sleep off his drunk in a cell."

Eagan leaped down from the wagon. "No, no, man! Can't you
see it's Kennedy?" he cried.

"What?" Acton exclaimed. "Kennedy?" He looked more closely. "Holy God! It is! Eagan what in the name of heaven has happened?"

Eagan told him quickly. Acton turned pale. He rubbed his hands together agitatedly. "I've ordered a platoon of soldiers up there. They'll be massacred." He turned to the driver, "Take your wagon to the side entrance. I'll have him carried in."

Acton hurried into the building. Soon, Kennedy was lying on a couch in the police surgeon's office. He was fully conscious and, with his wounds dressed and the blood washed away, he did not look quite as ghastly. He beckoned feebly to Acton.

"Tom, don't scatter our forces. Send out only strong details. Depend on Carpenter, Dilks and Leonard. They've handled mobs before. You must keep the telegraph open. Use Young and the Detective Bureau wherever you can," he whispered with great effort.

"Yes, John," Acton said. The police surgeon signaled Acton.

"He must rest now. You'll have to leave, Mr. Acton," the doctor said.

"Is he hurt badly?"

"A few ribs appear to be broken. If there are no complications—pneumonia, an injury to the lungs—he'll pull out fine. He's a tough old bird," the doctor said.

Acton left the room and hurried along the corridor. The safety of the city was in his hands. With Kennedy disabled, he commanded the Metropolitan Police. His thoughts raced ahead. He'd have to tell the Mayor what had happened. All available men must be rallied, troops brought in, militia mobilized. There was no hope of assembling a good-sized police force until later in the day. Meanwhile, the mob could run wild.

. . . 6

THE Lieutenant was young, barely twenty-two years old. He marched with a limp from a Minié ball that had pierced his right foot as he led his platoon in a futile charge up Marye's Heights. Behind him came forty Invalid Corps veterans. The officer—Lieutenant Abel Reade—had been ordered up from the Park Barracks to reinforce the police stationed at 677 Third Avenue. He had accepted the order with a soldier's stoicism.

Since reveille, whispers had been flying about the officers' mess, the guardroom, and the bivouac that trouble was in the making. Real trouble over the draft. Sentries had been doubled, and long before dawn the rebel prisoners had been removed to Riker's Island. Cannon covered the approaches to City Hall and the Park. All leaves had been canceled on orders from aged Mexican War hero Major General John E. Wool who commanded the Eastern Military District. At dawn, a detachment of United States Marines was ferried from the Brooklyn Navy Yard and posted around the Customs House in full battle dress. Units of the 12th Infantry at Fort Hamilton, the 3rd Infantry at Governor's Island, and the 47th New York Volunteers were alerted and had been standing under arms for immediate transport to Manhattan.

Highly fanciful rumors went scuttling around the Park Barracks: the rebs had a secret army hidden in the city; the rebs planned to spread bubonic plague by sending infected rats through the streets; reb agents equipped with new deadly poisons had contaminated Croton Reservoir.

Young Lieutenant Reade paid no attention to the agitated talk. He was a stolid man and had been in the field since the first days of the war, taking part in every major battle the Army of the Potomac had fought until his foot wound at Fredericksburg. He accepted nothing as fact until it was proven. He never questioned orders. The hardships of war, he endured with stoicism, facing each situation as it arose. He had never, under any circumstances, asked his men to do anything he would not undertake to do himself, and always set them an example of resolute courage.

In dealing with his enlisted men and noncommissioned officers, he was scrupulously fair, a stern disciplinarian who adhered to the letter of Army Regulations. Subordinates he treated with aloof politeness, but never disdainfully. His men spoke of him as a "decent shoulder strap"—high praise from enlisted men.

The march up Third Avenue went without incident until the column reached 14th Street. There, groups of shabbily dressed men and women gathered on the sidewalks to jeer at the soldiers. The Lieutenant ignored them and limped ahead, his light dress sword pressed against his shoulder in parade position.

As the platoon marched further uptown the roadway became more crowded with vehicles, and masses of people lined the curbs. Watchers leaned from windows to curse the soldiers, although there were occasional splatters of applause and a faint cheer or two. When the Lieutenant noticed the smoke from the mob-set fires he was convinced the platoon was heading into trouble. He raised his sword and in a drill field voice bellowed, "Platoon Front! Two ranks! On the double!"

The veterans trotted into the new formation—two lines extending across the roadway from curb to curb instead of the long, thin column of twos in which they had been marching. The soldiers picked their way around the stalled vehicles, still managing to keep a good alignment. Some were hardened, bearded campaigners with skins the texture of dried leather. Others were youths with a touch of the first down on their cheeks. But each of them had "seen the elephant"—which was

their way of describing combat. All had been wounded, a few
several times. Yet, despite their wounds and service on every
battlefield of the war, these men had re-enlisted in the Invalid
Corps to do garrison and guard duty in order to relieve men
more physically fit for the front.

As they pressed on, the spectators grew more overtly hostile.
Cries of "Dirty bayonets! Lincoln's butchers! Nigger lovers!"
were heard. At the corner of 39th Street, a man jumped out
into the roadway and threw a punch at the soldier closest to
him. The soldier nimbly dodged the blow and came up with
an adroit butt stroke. The musket stock shattered the attacker's
jaw. The man slumped to the cobblestones clutching his bloody
face.

The Lieutenant had seen this from the corner of his eye. He
decided to get tougher with this seedy looking rabble. He remembered too vividly how it had been at the beginning of the
war when mobs had attacked his regiment in Baltimore while
it was marching across the city to change trains for Washington.
This had the earmarks of the same thing. If a fight was coming,
he wanted his men prepared to meet it. Muskets at right shoulder shift was a fine position for parading, but not for fighting.

He faced his men and called out, "Port Arms!" The troops
snapped into that position without losing step and moved on
with muskets canted, long bayonets angled to the left. At 40th
Street, the smoke smell bit sharply and the mob exploded in a
spasm of violence. A fat, coarse-faced man, his shirt unbuttoned,
exposing curly black bristles of chest hair, jumped in front of
the Lieutenant. He was backed up by a score of men. He lunged
at the officer, grabbing for the sword.

"Give me that pig sticker, you lousy nigger lover!" he cried.

Without a flicker of expression the Lieutenant slashed a backhanded stroke with his sword. The blade left a deep, thinly
bleeding gash across the man's chest. He stumbled backwards,
frightened by the blood and the biting sting of sharp steel. His

friends surged toward the Lieutenant who lashed out left and right like an agile matador holding off frenzied bulls. The troops stood calmly awaiting orders. When the Lieutenant cleared a space, he shouted, "Stand back! We're coming through!"

"You goddamn tin soldier, you ain't worth a pinch of shit!" an enraged voice bawled.

"What the hell are we waiting for? Get those frigging soldiers now," a man cried wildly.

A barrage of bricks, bottles and stones showered about the soldiers. Most of the missiles flew over the ranks and landed among the great throng that closed in behind the platoon. The Lieutenant required no field manual to tell him that he was in a tight spot. Glowering rioters ringed his command and the circle was growing smaller. This was the moment for action. Even another second's delay might prove too late. The Lieutenant waved his sword. "Charge, bayonets! Charge!" he yelled.

The veterans dropped their muskets to the charge position. A battle cry ripped from forty throats as they rushed after the Lieutenant in a pell-mell attack. The sight of the bayonets and the cold-eyed soldiers checked the mob's will. The crowd broke as men slugged and clawed each other to make way for the soldiers. Some men crawled under the cars on hands and knees to escape. The mob parted like water before the prow of a clipper ship. There were hoarse cries, screams, and above the confused noise rose the pulsating cheers of the soldiers. The mass splintered into separate, thrashing fragments. Suddenly, the space of almost a block lay between the main body of the mob and the troops, with remnants dispersed along the Avenue.

The Lieutenant halted his panting men. The soldiers grinned at each other. This was work for real soldiers. The bayonet was the tool to take the fight out of a foe. Nobody could stand up before trained men who knew how to handle the "toothpicks."

The platoon re-formed and went on to 42nd Street. The men saw the unhampered fires raging. Flames had spread throughout the block between 46th and 47th Streets. The butcher's shack from which Andrews had made his speech was burning briskly. Sparks and cinders twisted crazily and fell in steady cascades.

At the corner of 42nd Street another hail of missiles crashed into the soldiers. Several men were hit. A stone tore the Lieutenant's cheek. He ignored the blood streaming from the gash. He lost none of his composure even when he realized that their position was hopeless: The mob was now engulfing his men. The encircling faces had lost all individuality; they were one face— open-mouthed and baleful.

The Lieutenant faced about and looked into the eyes of his soldiers. He read the despair in them and felt sorry for these veterans who had given so much. This was the end of the twisting road that had stretched from Bull Run to Gettysburg. A stone struck him in the back but he paid no attention to the blow. He regretted what had to be done—but felt no remorse. His duty was clear and released him from guilt.

"Rear rank, about face!" he ordered. He gave the command as if this were a parade ground in a training camp instead of a riot-torn street.

"Rear rank, shoulder arms! Front rank, shoulder arms!" he shouted.

The forty muskets were in firing position. "Both ranks—Fire!" he cried. The muskets cracked in unison. Black powder smoke mushroomed out and slowly drifted upwards to join the dark columns rising from the blazing buildings.

An incredulous, dismayed silence followed the shooting. A man screamed horribly. A woman shrieked. Complete chaos ensued. Bodies lay scattered in the street, some motionless, some still writhing; and bright red blood spurted.

The soldiers struggled with their long, clumsy muskets, reloading, biting cartridges, working rammers. An anguished cry came from the mob.

"Get the bastards before they can reload!" someone shouted.

Scattered pistol shots came from the mob. Two soldiers dropped.

"Fire at will!" the Lieutenant ordered.

Muskets popped sporadically, but it was a futile effort. The soldiers could not keep the mob from its vengeance. Rioters swarmed over the two ranks. The Lieutenant flayed with his sword until it snapped at the hilt. He pulled his revolver from the holster but before he could shoot, a paralyzing blow sent him to his knees. A boot caved in his ribs. In a strangely detached way he wondered about these people—why they were doing this to him and his men, why they hated so much. He had faced death so often on the battlefield that it was like an old friend. He was a soldier and prepared to die—but not here, not on a familiar street in his own city only a half mile from his home. The courage which had carried him up the slopes of Marye's Heights in the face of bullets and canister deserted him.

He pleaded for mercy until they battered him into silence.

. . . **7**

A S THIS upheaval convulsed the 21st Ward, no sign of it was visible anywhere else in the city. The suburbs lazed in summertime languor. And, in the city proper, children played on quiet streets the games that city children played: Prisoner's Base; Hopscotch; Red Rover, Red Rover.

The Park, an eleven-acre tract surrounding City Hall was one of New York's show places. Well-kept lawns were trimmed to billiard table smoothness and stately shade trees graced the open expanse. An ornate fountain stood at the Park's southern base. The area's open greenness was welcome in the clamor of Broadway. Directly across the busy thoroughfare was the elegant Astor House Hotel, and within the immediate vicinity stood famous amusement places like Barnum's Museum. Theaters, grand restaurants and great stores crowded the neighborhood. A block or so south was Printing House Square where the offices of important newspapers such as *The Times* and *The Tribune* were located.

The war had brought some slight alterations to the appearance of the Park. Rows of wooden barracks covered part of the eastern side—but everyone was aware this was merely a wartime measure and when hostilities ended these eyesores would be removed. Despite the unaesthetic army installations the Park still formed a splendid background for the graceful colonial style City Hall, surrounded by fine old trees which formed an arbor in the center of the lawn.

Promptly at 10:15 each morning, Mayor Opdyke strolled up the main path of the Park to his office in City Hall. This morning walk was almost a ritual with the Mayor and he missed it only in bad weather.

On leaving his home, the Mayor went south along Fifth Avenue, turned east at 8th Street and headed straight down Broadway to City Hall. He walked at a steady, leisurely pace, covering the distance to the Hall in about forty-five minutes. The Mayor liked to observe the activity on Broadway. He looked over the street with a proprietary air. He was Chief Executive of this city and thought of himself as the elected custodian of all this mercantile enterprise and splendor.

People along the way recognized him. He responded to their greetings with dignified nods, raising his hat to any ladies who passed. There were evidences of civic negligence that struck a few discordant notes. He was annoyed to see the street had not been properly swept, and became irritated at the condition of the roadway rutted with holes where paving blocks had worked loose and in which huge puddles remained long after the slightest rainfall—irksome deficiencies he could not eliminate because he was blocked by the Democrats in the city government.

Part of the opposition belonged to Tammany Hall. But a strong group was loyal to Fernando Wood and his Mozart Hall clique. The Mozarts and the Tammanies fought each other like alley cats squalling in a garbage heap—but managed to unite when it came to battling the Mayor.

As a result, streets went unpaved and unswept because the Democrats vetoed appropriations sought by the Street Commissioner, an Opdyke appointee. It was remarkable, with such internal dissension, that the city government was able to function at all.

On this hot, fateful day, Opdyke did not vary his routine. By 10:15 he was at his desk in the oak-paneled office on the ground floor of City Hall. His reception room was already filled with political hacks, party workers, favor seekers and a sprinkling of visitors who had bonafide business to transact. After Opdyke had seated himself in his comfortable leather chair he took a cigar case from his pocket, selected a Havana, lit it and settled back for the day's work. The day had started like all his days in City Hall. This evening, he would dine at Delmonico's and then go to see *Leah Forsook* the new comedy at the Winter Garden.

Opdyke was trying to keep his attention on the details of a printing contract being monotonously read by a prim City Hall clerk when the door of his office was flung open with great force. The startled Mayor looked up to see Detective Sergeant Young, pale and agitated, in the doorway.

"What's the matter with you, Young? Have you lost your mind, barging in here this way?" the Mayor asked testily.

"Mr. Mayor, a terrible riot has broken out in the 21st Ward

at Jenkins' office. The mob nearly beat Superintendent Kennedy to death," Young blurted.

Opdyke stared at him in dismay. "What? Are you sure?" he gasped.

"Yes, sir. Two of my detectives witnessed the whole affair. They tell me Jenkins' office and every building on the block is in flames. The mob is out of hand, they say. I believe you'd better come to Headquarters at once, sir."

"What's being done, Young?" the shocked Mayor asked.

"Well, sir, Commissioner Acton is in charge and he's contacted General Wool and General Sandford. Some regulars are coming in from Fort Hamilton and from Governor's Island—but they're only a handful. All police reserves have been recalled."

Opdyke rose slowly; his face was that of a stricken man. "I'll go with you, Sergeant." He glanced at the clerk who stood gaping at them. "Damn it, man! Don't stand there like a clod. Get transportation for us—my carriage!"

"Yes, sir," the clerk said, and scurried from the office.

"I have a buggy outside," Young said.

"And a fast horse—I hope," Opdyke said, seeking to mask his agitation with a weak smile.

A few minutes later, people in the vicinity of City Hall turned to look curiously at their Mayor clinging to the hand straps of a careening buggy that raced up Center Street, the driver standing on the footboard whipping up the horse. There had been rumors all morning about some disturbance in the upper part of the city. These uneasy reports flared anew when word of the Mayor's hasty departure spread around. The disorders on the docks earlier and the traffic jam along Park Row which indicated Third Avenue was blocked, gave credence to the vague whispers. Even more disquieting was the police cordon around City Hall and the squads of soldiers on constant patrol in the Park, as artillerymen lounged by cannon mounted to sweep the walks.

Knots of excited clerks, shopkeepers and pedestrians gathered. Overly cautious merchants who had experienced riots before lowered the iron shutters of their shop windows. A company of regulars landed at South Ferry and marched up Broadway to Police Headquarters. Tension grew and even the most
skeptical agreed that trouble impended. Foreboding settled over
the streets like a poisonous fog. Men hurried about their business with worried faces. Gradually, traffic on Broadway slackened until, almost magically, there was none at all and the city
fell silent. Sidewalks were no longer thronged with busy people. The streets were deserted and this empty stillness grew
even more frightening than the menacing clamor of the mob uptown.

. . . *8*

THE doors of Police Headquarters were guarded by uniformed policemen and armed civilian clerks. The basement
had turned into a humming base of operations. Sweating, shirt-
sleeved telegraphers worked their keys with flying fingers as
they dispatched hastily dictated messages. Mayor Opdyke nervously paced the floor, chewing on an unlit cigar. Commissioner
Acton and his chief clerk, Seth Hawley, sat at a long table with
a gaunt white-haired Brigadier General who looked like Andrew
Jackson. He was Brevet Brigadier Harvey Brown, a veteran
regular: West Point, Class of '18, with a good record in the
Seminole War, the Mexican War, and distinguished service at
the start of the Civil War. The sixty-seven-year-old officer, whose

permanent rank was Colonel, 5th U.S. Artillery, commanded the forts and harbor defenses of New York City. He was embittered that the War Department had removed him from field duty and sidetracked him where there was little likelihood of ever seeing action again. At the first call for troops, the old soldier had sniffed gunpowder, and buckling on sword and pistol, had come in from Governor's Island with the leading units of regulars.

He reported directly to Acton as he had been ordered by Major General John E. Wool, bringing with him detachments of the 3rd and 12th U.S. Infantry regiments. Brown set up his command post at Police Headquarters and notified Wool of his arrival. From his own office, the Eastern Military Department, Elm Street Arsenal, Wool dispatched a message to Brown plac-ing him in charge of United States troops in the city and order-ing him to co-operate fully with the police in the suppression of the riot.

Immediately upon receipt of this notification, Brown issued a communique:

HEADQUARTERS, NEW YORK   July 13, 1863
ORDERS #1:—

In obedience to the orders of the Major General commanding the Eastern Department, undersigned assumes command of United States troops in this city. Lt. Col. Frothingham and Captain Revelle are of the staff of the undersigned and will be obeyed accordingly.

                                            Harvey Brown
                                            Brigadier General

A copy of this was delivered to the Seventh Avenue Arsenal where aged Major General Charles Sandford who commanded the New York State Militia had established his headquarters. Although the General's rank stemmed from long militia service, he resented what to his mind was usurpation of command by Brown, a mere brigadier and a brevet at that. Sandford, a no-toriously crotchety man, was jealous of his two stars; the mere

thought that a one-star man was to be his superior sent him
into a temper tantrum.

He did more than rant. He locked up his militia behind the
thick walls of the Arsenal and sat sulking. However, a platoon
of the 3rd Infantry Regiment was mixed in with the state troops.
The young lieutenant commanding the platoon had mistakenly
marched his men to the Arsenal instead of Police Headquarters.
Irascible Sandford refused to release these regulars despite
Brown's many requests for them.

The mess became more muddled when General Wool in attempting to clarify the situation sent an ambiguous message:

HEADQUARTERS, NEW YORK   July 13, 1863
SPECIAL ORDERS:—

All troops called out for the protection of the city are placed under
the command of General Sandford whose orders they will strictly
obey.

By Command of:
Maj. Gen. John E. Wool
C. T. Christiansen, Capt., ADC

When this reached General Brown he showed that his temper was equal to Sandford's. He thumped the table top and
swore that no regular would take orders from any damned mili-
tiaman like Sandford. He insisted that Wool's order applied only
to those troops specifically mustered for this emergency and did
not refer to regulars. Acton tried to calm the General and had
almost succeeded, when a telegram for Brown came from Sandford:

General Brown:
The entire military force at Police Headquarters will be sent to the
Seventh Avenue Arsenal and report to Major General Sandford.

Charles W. Sandford
Major General

Brown loosed a barrage of profanity gleaned from more than
forty active years in the army. Between rounds of curses the

angry General told Acton and everyone else within earshot that he was "damned sick and tired of such treatment," and wouldn't be pushed around by any blankety blank armchair general.

"For all I care the rebels can burn this goddamn city. Let Sandford run the show. I'm through!" he bellowed.

When the General finally ran out of breath, Acton aided by Opdyke and Seth Hawley again tried to placate him. They managed to keep him from walking out, and convinced him that an honorable settlement might be negotiated.

Hawley, an intelligent, diplomatic gentleman, was sent to the Arsenal to repair the rift. The clerk mollified cranky old Sandford and even persuaded him to release the platoon of regulars with which he triumphantly returned to Headquarters. No one ever noted what Brown said to the poor Lieutenant who had made the inept blunder.

After restoring the missing men to Brown, Hawley dashed down to Elm Street and conferred with Wool. More than seventy years old, Wool was a befuddled man. He had gained honor in the Mexican War but was long past his prime. He grudgingly admitted that the error was his and that his order should have been worded more clearly. As Brown had argued, General Wool's intentions were for him to command all United States troops whether Volunteers or regulars, while Sandford was to lead the militia only.

The peevish controversy was finally settled, but while it raged no troops took action against the rioters. Mulberry Street was a scene of boiling activity. A battery of artillery drawn by slavering horses tore around a corner, the gunners clinging to the rocking caisson. A squad of regulars, followed by a wagon loaded with ammunition, marched down the cobbled street. From another direction came a company of marines bent under full packs slogging to a halt at the steps of the building. Detachments of police hurried in and out of the place. Mounted couriers galloped up, leaping from their horses at full tilt. Troops erected crude barricades and the neighborhood took on the appearance of a street in a besieged city.

Men from Captain Porter's detail and Invalid Corps soldiers who had borne the mob's assaults straggled into Headquarters. Each man had undergone harrowing experiences. It was amazing that any one of them had managed to escape alive as the rioters had showed no mercy to policemen or soldiers trapped by them. Most survivors needed medical care. There were too many for the three police surgeons on duty to attend and a call went out for available doctors.

The lobby of the building soon looked like a front line dressing station. Doctors with bloody hands and splotched white coats went from casualty to casualty swabbing, bandaging, stitching. The air reeked with the mingled odors of carbolic acid, liniment and blood. Bits of clothing, bloodstained bandages and other debris littered the floor. Men in hobnailed boots, spitting tobacco juice, stomped on the polished planks and left scuff marks in the once gleaming wood. Lounging soldiers and policemen sat around calmly smoking pipes and chatting easily with each other while awaiting orders. Women of the neighborhood volunteered. Some acted as nurses, while others staffed the field kitchen that had been set up in the street, and steaming pots of coffee were soon ready. Ambulances from the big city hospitals rolled up to cart away the wounded and occasionally a corpse.

Terrified Negroes flocked to Headquarters for refuge as they fled from brutal gangs which roved the streets to beat any colored person—man, woman or child, young or old. Acton was determined to protect the Negroes from such cruelty and despatched a telegram:

> To All Precincts:
> Receive every colored person. Refuse no one.
> Acton.

But even more pressing than the safety of the Negroes from Acton's point of view were the reports of wholesale looting and the wanton burning of private homes. The Mayor had become increasingly upset with each fresh notice of destruction. When Thomas Lowery, of Young's Detective Bureau, turned up with the alarming word that a mob was marching on Marston's Gun Factory at 21st Street and Second Avenue, Opdyke grew very agitated: here, he himself was financially involved.

The weapons stored in the armory above the workshop was a vital target for the rioters. The arms must be kept from the mob.

A message was rushed to the 18th Precinct on East 22nd Street, ordering that a force be sent to defend Marston's. The Broadway Squad, thirty-two hand-picked six-footers renowned for their fighting prowess, made up a portion of the complement in the 18th Precinct. Captain John Cameron, commanding the station house, sent these rugged giants into the building, led by a Sergeant Burdick.

The policemen were armed with carbines in addition to their revolvers and sticks. They took up vantage points in the factory and awaited the mob. They did not have long to wait. The mob soon came. It numbered almost ten thousand screaming, gesturing men and women. Even some children came along to help storm the building. At first, they seemed to have no plan of attack and merely threw rocks at the windows or fired pistols and muskets indiscriminately.

But after the fight had been underway for a little time, a group of forty to fifty men armed with muskets formed military lines and, at the command of a man in workingman's clothing fired at the defenders in carefully aimed volleys. Ross Lane and his detachment had arrived.

The police fought as well and as long as they could. At one point, several rioters broke in through a side door. They were led by "Big Tim," the horseman who had appeared on Third

Avenue at the height of the outbreak outside the Marshal's office. A policeman dropped him with a carbine shot which killed the man immediately. The others fled, dragging the body with them.

The attacks continued for almost two hours. At last, around 4:00 P.M., it became obvious that the small force of police could no longer hold out. Most of the officers were nicked by bullets, although none had been seriously wounded. Burdick decided to withdraw. He told his men they had done all that was humanly possible and that further resistance was futile.

Abandoning the building was a ticklish problem. No policeman could possibly have made his way through that howling mob. The men pondered the question of retreat, which was finally solved when Burdick spotted a ventilation hole in the rear wall, about twelve inches by eighteen inches in diameter, extending through the wall to a point eighteen feet above the ground. Despite their size the men of the Broadway Squad squeezed through the pipe one by one, feet first, and on emerging from the hole dropped the distance to a littered back yard. In a body, they ran through the yard, scaled a fence, cut through a stoneyard and went at top speed toward the station house. A group of some fifty rioters spotted them and tried to cut the policemen off.

The police made short shrift of them with their locust sticks. The rioters fled and the officers went to the precinct house, where Captain Cameron ordered them to change into civilian clothes and get down to Mulberry Street where they were urgently needed.

The mob soon had cause to regret its victory, which proved to be short-lived and tragic. No sooner had the last man of the Broadway Squad left the building than the rioters beat down the doors and charged inside. Men and women surged up the stairs to the armory storeroom on the third floor where most of the weapons were kept. In minutes, excited people were swarming all over, grabbing guns and stuffing their pockets with ammunition. The downstairs part was packed with frenzied individuals who smashed up machinery and everything that was breakable. Still another part of the crowd milled about in the street.

Coincidentally, almost a hundred policemen, who had been gathered from several precincts, were marching down toward Police Headquarters when they came upon this scene. With the Metropolitans were men who had been at the Marshal's office—including battered and seething Captain Porter. The men were itching for revenge. Here was their chance. The mob was so intent on the proceedings within the building that none noticed what was going on a block away.

Porter led the police at the rioters on the double. Before the mob was even aware of their presence the officers were flailing away with their sticks. Wrathful police cleared a path to the doors of the building, pitilessly clubbing all who came within range of the punishing sticks. Rioters rushed out to aid their friends only to fall beneath the clubs. Some were killed on the spot.

Suddenly anguished screaming was heard from those still inside the rickety old frame structure. Somehow, the only staircase in the building had been set ablaze. Terrified people tried to get out of the building. Within moments, the entire lower portion of it was aflame. The police did not hit anyone escaping the fire unless he was armed. Anyone with a carbine was clubbed without mercy.

Scores of rioters on the upper floors were hopelessly trapped by the blaze. The stairway collapsed and those on the third floor were doomed. Many leaped from windows, cracking their skulls on the pavement. The shrieking and screaming was hellish as only a few managed to escape before the ancient flooring collapsed, plunging everyone into the maelstrom of fire. To add to the horror, cases of small-arms ammunition were set off, the explosions sending showers of sparks and bullets whistling in every direction. The spectacle was so ghastly and the smell of burning flesh so strong that even the policemen sickened and tried desperately to save those they could. . . .

The attack on the Armory was regarded as particularly significant at Police Headquarters. Had the rioters been able to retain the arms the results would have been fatal. Thousands of armed insurgents would surely have overwhelmed the city's defenders. There had been at least one disciplined group among the attackers, which gave a sound basis to the belief that Confederate agents were actively engaged in the outbreak.

Further sources of worry were the reports of far-flung destruction by separate mobs. On Eleventh Avenue, the tracks of the Harlem Railroad were torn up for several blocks, stalling all inbound trains on that line. The entire street front on Broadway between 28th and 29th Streets was razed when gangs set Provost Marshal Mannierre's draft office on fire. A roving mob was ransacking wealthy homes on Lexington Avenue. Another mob set fire to the Bull's Head Hotel on East 44th Street, gutting the premises. The cattle in the stockade had stampeded and knocked over the barriers and terrified steers were running loose in the streets.

HE Colored Orphan Asylum occupied the entire block be-
T tween 43rd and 44th Streets on Fifth Avenue. It stood on
a good-sized plot, the big house surrounded by trees and grass.
The main building was a fine rambling old structure painted
white with green shutters on the tall windows. The lawns were
well trimmed and giant shade trees spread their branches to
form a leafy canopy over the gravel carriage path that ran in
a sweeping circle from the entrance gate.

Philanthropical New Yorkers supported the institution which
cared for two hundred to three hundred children. The supervisor, a white man named William E. Davis, had a competent
and kindly staff to help him run the place, which was a source
of civic pride and a symbol of communal good will. The Asylum
and its happy children was a favored charity and the youngsters
received excellent treatment.

The sudden invasion of a mob caught the Asylum authorities
by surprise. Rioters had climbed the picket fence that encircled
the grounds and swarmed all over, trampling flower beds and
ruining the orphanage's vegetable patch. Davis saw at once the
potential menace of this ugly crowd. He was a resolute man
not easily intimidated. He confronted the rioters and demanded
to know their business on private property.

"We're here to clean out your nigger nest," a pock-faced man
bawled.

"Let us get our hands on the little niggers," a woman cried.

"Stop all this damned talk and burn the place down," a drunk
yelled.

This suggestion was greeted by a chorus of approval, but no
one made a move toward the house although only Davis blocked
the way. Somehow, not even this mob could bring itself to hurt

the children who stood at the windows, little faces pressed against the panes, eyes wide with fright.

Davis seized on the mob's hesitation and argued with the rioters, urging them to leave. When he saw that all his reasoning was vain he pleaded for time to get the inmates safely out of the building.

"Surely, you don't want the blood of these poor children on your hands," he pleaded.

His entreaties finally carried some weight with the self-appointed leaders of the mob. They had a brief conference and decided to let Davis have five minutes to evacuate the children—then the mob would take over and burn the building.

Davis ran into the orphanage. In minutes the staff had organized the children and were marching them out in two files. No sooner was the place emptied than the van of the mob poured in, the rioters fighting among themselves to be first in the looting. A large, drunken group became infuriated at the sight of the Negro youngsters. Whooping and screeching, they charged across the lawn to get at the orphans. Fortunately a company of firemen, led by Chief Engineer John Decker, came down Fifth Avenue at this moment, hauling hose carts and pumpers. The fire fighters with Decker were a special unit far above the usual run of volunteers in character and intelligence—although equal to any in a brawl.

Instantly Decker ordered his men to drive the mob away from the children. The firemen, using spanners and hose nozzles, barreled into the mob and sent the rioters scurrying. The children were formed into a compact group and Decker deployed his men around them. The firemen took the axes and hook poles from their carts and prepared to defend the youngsters.

Angered by the firemen's presence, the mob deliberately set out to destroy the old house. As women ran in and out lugging pillowcases filled with silverware and crockery, others were stealing clothing, bedding, furniture and even toys. Rioters cursed and passed around whisky bottles. Soon fights broke out over some worthless piece of furniture or a piece of worn clothing. At the height of the looting somebody set the parlor curtains afire. The flames leaped to life, firing the place into a holocaust. If Decker and his men had tried to fight the fire, the children would have been left unguarded and at the mercy of the mob. They were forced, therefore, to watch in impotent fury as the building blazed.

Trees near the house caught fire and flared up like tall torches. The walls and roof caved in and the house collapsed with a rending crash. Flying sparks and flaming pieces of debris started a dozen brush fires. But, despite this destruction, the rioters had not yet had enough. They stood in surly gangs, glowering at the children, trying to work up the courage to attack them in spite of the firemen.

The women goaded the men on, swept up in a savage frenzy. The men shook fists and cursed the firemen. One waved a pistol and swore to "blast Decker and his damn red shirts to Hell." Those most distant from the volunteers made the loudest threats.

A bony, mad-looking man with hair hanging to his shoulders who was dressed in tatters shrilled in a cracked voice, "Kill the black bastards! It's the Lord's will!" He was a Five Points derelict known as "Crazy Jerry." Some said he was a defrocked priest who had gone mad.

Because they were afraid to fight the firemen, the rioters brawled among themselves. One man slashed at another with his switch blade knife. He missed the thrust, and lurching drunkenly, plunged the blade into the breast of a young Paradise Square whore, killing her instantly. No one even noticed the unfortunate girl's death except a pimp named "Little Soapie." He squatted beside the body and wept. She had been his best money maker.

At last, a crowd of about a hundred started toward the firemen and the orphans. This gang was led by a lumbering, slope-shouldered rough who advanced some paces ahead of the rest, waving them on with a thick arm. The others followed him in a pack. As they came closer, Decker moved toward them, his big fist curled around the handle of a heavy spanner.

"I'm warning you—stay where you are," Decker called.

"Get the hell out of our way, Decker," the leader growled.

Decker eyed him calmly. "I recognize you, Jack Rioraty. And as God is my witness, I'll brain you if you take another step."

Rioraty stopped short and the oncoming men faltered. They glanced at each other furtively. Actually, they had no real taste for fighting the firemen. Rioraty waved a derogatory hand at the chief engineer and said, "All right, you nigger lover. Keep your pickaninnies." He turned to the men behind him. "Come on, lads. This ain't a place for white men. Let's leave Decker and his nigger babies."

A man edged close to Rioraty. "There's richer pickings for us, Jack—why waste time on them?" He spat toward the orphans.

"What's on your mind, Toomy, lad?" Rioraty asked.

"We'll go downtown along Fifth where the rich bastards are. And we'll make ourselves a real haul."

"Good!" Rioraty cried, glancing sideways at Decker, grateful for this easy out.

"Burn out Opdyke! He's got plenty!" a man shouted.

"That's it! That's it!" the rioters exclaimed.

"On our way, lads! Burn out all the rich sons of bitches!" Rioraty cried. A yell rose up from the rioters as word spread of their intentions. They fell in behind Rioraty, staggering off in a cursing, disorganized mass. The women trailed after, shrieking insults at the firemen. A group of them tied a rope around the dead whore and dragged her body with them. The corpse was found floating in the East River several hours later. The mob was soon gone, leaving smoldering ruins and dread in its wake.

Decker faced his men. "We'd better get these kids to the station house," he said, wearily. He looked after the mob. "What makes them like this? Don't they have kids and families of their own?"

He turned and walked slowly away, followed by the orphanage staff and the frightened children who came in a file of twos, hand in hand. The firemen brought up the rear, hauling their equipment. Flames still danced along the charred timbers of the house. The scorched trees stood like cindery skeletons. Only a short distance away from this ravaged place was Central Park where the trees were richly green, unscathed by fire and unmarred by violence. Yet, even in the Park, the smell of burning was in the air and smoke drifted down into the foliage.

. . . *10*

LATE in the afternoon, Inspector Dan Carpenter was given the chance he had been wanting all day. A detective reported that a huge mob was coming straight down Broadway to attack Police Headquarters. The ultimate aim of this throng was the financial district where it could loot the banks and even the subtreasury.

Just prior to this, word had come that a band of young roughs had attempted to sack Opdyke's house but were foiled by Ben Mannierre and a number of the Mayor's neighbors who had turned out, fully armed, to drive the looters away. After fleeing Opdyke's, this gang united with others and joined the big mob moving to the heart of the downtown section. The showdown was coming.

Commissioner Acton understood that this mob must be defeated or else anarchy would sweep New York and spread into its environs. There had been minor outbreaks in Brooklyn and even in points as far off as Jamaica, Long Island. Bergen and Folk had crushed the Brooklyn outbreak with one hundred policemen and a few troops, but the danger was not yet over.

Telegrams had been dispatched to the Governors of New Jersey, Connecticut, and Massachusetts asking them to rush whatever troops were on hand into New York City. A wire had gone out to Governor Seymour notifying him of the uprising and urging him to return immediately. The Mayor had also sent a pressing message to Secretary of War, Edward Stanton, in Washington, describing the disorders and appealing to the government for aid in quelling them.

The prime question was how to deal with the mob on Broadway. Acton could hold Carpenter and his men at Headquarters to stave off the attack or else send the force to meet the rioters in the streets. He decided on the latter course. He felt the sight of a powerful police detail marching in the open would be a show of strength. The gamble that Carpenter's men could win had to be taken. Every fit policeman was given orders to join Carpenter; the marines and soldiers were left behind to guard the Headquarters building.

A thinly strung line of troops and leathernecks deployed in the street. They made breastworks by turning carts on their sides and knelt behind them with loaded muskets. A battery of light artillery moved into firing position. Under the crisp commands of Drill Officer John Copeland, the policemen formed into a column of fours. Carpenter addressed them briefly from the steps of the building. He was a sturdy man, with a florid face, a bristling mustache and fierce black eyes.

"Men! We are going to meet and put down a mob! We will take no prisoners! We must strike quick and strike hard!" Carpenter said.

The policemen cheered. Carpenter gave a sign to Copeland who bawled, "By the right flank! Company front! March!" The men stepped out smartly and Carpenter trotted to his position in the front rank, several yards ahead. The marines and soldiers raised their caps and saluted the police with a lusty shout.

As the detachment marched away, General Brown and Commissioner Acton stood side by side. Still disgruntled from his run-in with Sandford and Wool, the General managed a thin smile at Acton. "Good lads, those," he said.

"The best," Acton agreed. "I pray God they all return safely." With that, the Commissioner walked slowly into the building. He paused in the lobby wondering what the next few hours would bring. Understanding Acton's tensions, the old General relieved his own by inspecting the troops. They were well posted and he was satisfied, but he did find a young soldier standing sentry duty without a bayonet on his musket. Brown, almost gleefully, gave the unlucky private a tongue-lashing—and no matter what his other shortcomings might have been, Brown was unequaled when it came to the use of strong language. He left the shaken soldier and continued on his rounds feeling elated, humming "Green Grow the Lilacs, Oh," which had been his favorite song since the Mexican War. The very hint of possible action was tonic enough for the crusty old soldier.

From Union Square to Bond Street, the mob controlled Broadway. The motley crowd progressed slowly downtown, and ahead of it, like refugees from a flood, came little groups of Negroes trying to escape. The voices of the rioters blended into a roar heard for blocks around.

As he led his men along at a good pace, Inspector Carpenter heard the mob. His men heard it, too, long before they could even glimpse it. Fingers gripped locust sticks more tightly. Men clenched their teeth and drew their lips into hard lines, but showed no signs of faltering or hesitation. The cadence of the police march was unbroken and nothing in the bearing of the men indicated that the mob sounds had any effect.

Without its hosts of shoppers and sight-seers Broadway seemed alien. Here and there cautious faces peered through the slats of shuttered windows. Shops were silent, doors and windows barred. Clusters of tense people crowded the hotel lobbies and watched in silence as the grim Metropolitans marched by. Well-dressed men openly displayed revolvers. And in the saloons where the wealthy gathered for afternoon refreshments the atmosphere was oppressively gloomy.

Most commercial houses and factories had either dismissed their employees for the day or else were on strike so that little business was being conducted. In some shops—mainly the iron foundries—the workers did not sympathize with the mobs and stayed at their machines arming themselves with any weapons that were handy. In several of the large stores on lower Broadway, Lord and Taylor's for one, male clerks formed a defense group to guard the premises. All military passes and leaves had been canceled and personnel ordered to report at Police Headquarters. Officers in uniform hurried through side streets on the way to Mulberry Street with naked swords or loaded revolvers.

The police and the mob drew closer to each other. A few times, Carpenter was forced to halt his men and make way for wagon loads of refugees. Streams of pitiful Negroes stumbled downtown, most of them waiters from Broadway restaurants which the rioters had raided. Upward spiraling smoke marked where stores and buildings had been set afire by the mob.

The main body of the mob met the police head-on between Bond and Amity Streets. When he saw the solid phalanx of rioters, Carpenter stared in momentary incredulity. The mob was made up of thousands and stretched back up Broadway. A bearded, one-eyed man who was carrying a bludgeon stood in the fore of this awesome throng. Behind him came scores of men armed with lead pipes, pick handles and iron bars. Women mingled in the huge crowd and dotted throughout were placards lettered "NO DRAFT." Nothing like this mob had ever been seen in New York City before.

When the rioters viewed the police force, a hush fell on the noisy demonstrators. Although the mob outnumbered the Metropolitans thirty or forty to one, none dared make the first move against the hard-faced and determined policemen: this was a mob; its courage came from the mass, not from individuals.

The mob stumbled to a ragged halt. Those in front began backing away, but the rear of the crowd kept pressing forward. This caused a tangled pile-up, and confusion spread among them.

Carpenter sensed this was the right moment to attack. He pointed with his locust stick and cried, "Up, Guards! At them!" He rushed at the bearded man who led the mob and killed him with a blow of his club. The police ranks charged into the mass and the battle was on. An unearthly cry came from the rioters. Bricks and other missiles rained on the police but miraculously not a single officer was struck. The cruel locust sticks rose and fell almost in unison as though someone was giving the tempo for the attack.

The resistance of the mob was surprisingly feeble once it came to grips with the police. Men dropped to their knees and begged for mercy—but none was given them. The Metropolitans had seen comrades injured; they showed no pity. The deadly sticks sent hundreds to the pavement with crushed skulls. Any rioter who dared fight back was clubbed down. In minutes, the mighty mob dissolved into screaming segments running in every direction. Women as well as men pitched senseless to the cobblestones. Some died there in the gutter. Hundreds fled from Broadway to cower in doorways but no hiding place could shield them from the vengeance of the police. Men with broken arms, smashed heads, torn and bleeding scalps, staggered away.

Soon, the mob was in full flight. The triumphant police gave pursuit and beat anyone who could not run fast enough. The murderous outcries of the rioters were replaced by piteous groans. Those in the rear who were still unscathed threw their weapons aside and fled whimpering.

When Carpenter had satisfied himself that this particular mob had been rendered harmless he ordered his men back into line. The police marched down Broadway again in serried ranks. As soon as they had left, rioters crept back to carry off their dead and wounded. A detail of police left behind by Carpenter did not hinder them in this work.

All along the line of march shutters flew open. People lined the steps of homes and hotels to cheer the Metropolitans. Carpenter's florid face was flushed with exaltation. This was a fine revenge for the earlier defeats the police had suffered, and cheering news to bring to Acton at the embattled Headquarters.

. . . *11*

A STRONG pleasant breeze was blowing in from the ocean. It tempered the heat and made the sun-bright day comfortable. Puffy, white clouds drifted lazily across the otherwise flawless blue sky and, for the moment, Horatio Seymour, Governor of New York State, forgot his cares of office, the deplorable condition of New York City's harbor defenses, and his worry over the draft which he felt was so unjust. He swayed gently in an old-fashioned Boston rocker on the porch of the gracious house known as "Woodland" which was owned by Mr. and Mrs. James Nielsen, his wife's cousins.

His hasty survey of New York's harbor installations had afforded him no pleasure and only added to his anxieties. The city was guarded by outmoded, undermanned forts equipped with obsolete armament. New York's safety depended on the works at the Narrows, Staten Island, Governor's Island, and the antiquated batteries on Bedloe's and Ellis Islands. The Governor feared that a flotilla of Confederate ironclad raiders one day would sweep into the harbor, steam past Fort Hamilton and Fort Lafayette on one side of the Narrows and Fort Tompkins and Fort Richmond on the other without even being hit by the rusting cannon of the crumbling forts. Once safely by these pitiful barriers, the ironclads could turn their guns on the city itself and the shipping that jammed the port.

The state of the naval units in the harbor area was scarcely more encouraging. A few small gunboats and a venerable frigate were the only vessels available to oppose a sea-borne attack. These hulks would merely provide target practice for the gun crews of an ironclad. The Governor's survey, accompanied by irascible General Brown, who commanded the forts, and grouchy, dropsical General Wool, had scarcely tended to put him at ease. Brown grumbled about his assignment and Wool rambled on about his Mexican War experiences throughout the tour.

Seymour was convinced that a Confederate raid was a distinct possibility. It was known that the rebels were building huge rams in Scottish shipyards—ironclads more powerful than the world had ever known. With these warships there would be practically no gamble in a naval attack on New York.

The stakes were high enough for the Confederates to take any risk. The great Brooklyn Navy Yard was vulnerable, as were the shipyards along the East River front where, among others, the giant ram "Dunderberg," an ironclad of the latest type, was under construction at the Neptune works. It was worth any hazard to destroy this ram alone.

Rear Admiral Hiram Paulding, commandant of the Navy Yard, agreed with Seymour. The crusty sailor saw the picture darkly. "Any time the rebs feel like coming, they'll get here. I can't stop them with old scows. Not in the harbor, in the Bay, or on the rivers."

After his inspection, Seymour held a conference with the top city officials to discuss the predicament. Everyone concurred that an attack would be disastrous, but were inclined to do nothing about safeguarding against one. The general attitude was that since the rebs had not attacked after two years, they were never coming.

Opdyke had been pleasant enough but seemed little concerned with Seymour's suggestion that the forts be strengthened by replacing the obsolete ordnance with rifled cannon and heavy caliber naval guns. The military brass nodded sagely, Paulding gave the idea his support, copious notes were taken, but Seymour knew with glum certainty that nothing concrete would really be done. Inertia, ineptness and complacency had corroded these men.

The meeting had only added to the irksome nature of his visit. There had also been some vague talk of violent opposition to the draft. This had been pooh-poohed by the officials who chose to believe that such reports had been planted by Copperheads to create dissension and unrest.

But all that seemed remote now as he dozed in the sun. At dusk, Nielsen drove him to a restaurant near Long Branch where a reception was being held in the Governor's honor. Since this was an all-male affair, Mrs. Nielsen stayed at home. At 10:00 o'clock, she was preparing to retire when Tim Simpkins, the local telegraph operator, mounted on a sweating horse, galloped up the carriage drive. He informed the maid who responded to his knock that he had a telegram for Governor Seymour. Mrs. Nielsen hurried downstairs and told him where he could find the Governor, if the wire was very urgent.

"Oh, it's urgent, all right," the messenger said. "The rebs are burning New York City." Without any further explanation, Simpkins dashed out, remounted his horse and galloped off in a swirl of dust. Mrs. Nielsen and the maid stared at each other mutely and then peered into the languid summer darkness, trying to imagine the glaring fires that were ravaging New York.

The Governor's reception was one of those long-winded affairs which featured after-dinner addresses by both prominent and obscure politicians since the chairman of the arrangements committee had no wish to offend anyone by not including him on the speakers' list. The oratory followed a sumptuous shore dinner of boiled lobster drenched in butter sauce, baked clams, succulent steamers, shrimp and other seafood for which the Jersey shore was noted.

From the dais where he sat at the head table, filled with good food and lulled by the boring speeches, Seymour stared over the audience with stony, heavy lidded eyes. A curtain of cigar smoke drifted to the ceiling. The guests were bluff, hearty men. The older ones wore full beards while the younger ones, many in uniform, sported the fashionable mutton-chop whiskers—a style preferred by Seymour. The speaker was drawing to a close and Seymour realized, with a start, that he was next on the program. The Governor was a fine speechmaker and knew how to captivate an audience. Even skeptical auditors were won to him when he greeted a gathering with his hearty and characteristic salutation—"My Friends"—delivered with warmth and sincerity.

The sweaty speaker wound up his talk with a flourish. His eloquence was rewarded by mild applause. The guests shifted in their chairs, readjusted their clothing, signaled waiters for more brandy, lit fresh cigars and belched politely. The toastmaster rose to introduce Seymour. In keeping with the custom of the times, his introduction was flowery and elegant. The toastmaster was just warming up to his eulogy when Tim Simpkins burst headlong into the restaurant, covered with dust from his long ride. He rushed up to Seymour and handed him the telegram. The guests jumped to their feet buzzing with excitement.

The Governor opened the envelope. One glance at the neatly penned message drained the color from his face. He regained his composure quickly and said to Simpkins, "You made no mistake in transcribing this?"

"No, Governor. I sure wish to hell it was a mistake," the man replied.

Seymour turned to Nielsen. "Bad news, Jim. There's rioting in New York over the draft. I must return there immediately."

"But, Horatio—there's no train until midnight. And a mighty slow one at that. Six hours to New York," Nielsen said.

The Governor took an ornate gold watch from his vest pocket. He snapped open the hunter case. "Just a quarter to eleven. How long will it take to reach the depot, Jim?"

"About half an hour. But I can't let you go this way. Your valise——"

"Send it on to me." Seymour beckoned to the telegrapher, scribbled hastily on a piece of paper and handed it to the man. "Get this off to Mayor Opdyke in New York City, at once," he said.

"Right, sir. Soon as I get back to my office."

Seymour made hasty good-bys and left the restaurant. He climbed into Nielsen's buggy as his host took the reins. The guests crowded into the doorway wondering aloud about the reasons for the Governor's hasty departure. The telegraph operator told them. He gave the story his own touches, vividly depicting the total destruction of New York. Fortunately, he was more reliable as a telegrapher than a reporter, and promptly dispatched Seymour's brief message to Opdyke. The Governor stated that he was taking the first train and hoped to arrive at the Cortlandt Street ferry about 6:00 A.M.

As he paced the wooden platform, waiting for the train, Seymour's active mind was filled with the steps that must be taken to quell the disturbances. He would order the mayors of nearby cities to rush troops and police to New York. The militia regiments would be recalled from Pennsylvania if the War Department were willing to release them. Volunteer deputies would be sworn in and issued arms.

Suddenly, he thought that this must be some trick of his political enemies, who for muddy reasons, were exaggerating the danger of the outbreak. He had a burst of bitterness against Opdyke and all the overstuffed nonentities of his administration. Indolent, pompous men who had allowed the city to grow as helpless as a plump partridge with a broken wing, and at the first hint of trouble were bawling for the Governor to extricate them from the mess they had made for themselves.

The Mayor was an ineffectual bore. The commanding Generals, Brown and Wool, were doddering refugees from an old men's home. The whole city was in a mess. And of all the chuckleheaded errors the Lincoln government had committed, this draft was the worst. Personally, Seymour respected Lincoln as a man of resourcefulness and high purpose—but capable of what he considered ridiculous blunders, such as replacing General McClellan with a succession of idiots, persecuting Democrats like Clement Vallandigham and signing a law as tyrannical as the National Conscription Act. The draft was immoral and the three-hundred-dollar exemption clause a blot on the national honor.

Seymour's thoughts became increasingly gloomy. He paced the platform with impatient fury, ignoring Nielsen and a small group of well-wishers who had come to see him off. He heard the train whistle far in the distance. He stopped his striding and tried to calm himself. In six hours or so he would be in New York and would learn, firsthand, how bad the situation was. In all fairness, no matter what he might think of them as executives, Opdyke and the members of the Police Board, men like Acton and Bergen were not cowards. There was trouble in the city—even though the Republicans might make it seem worse than it was. Well, he thought, he would know soon enough. If the Republicans were trying to make him dance to their tune, they'd find he knew a trick or two. If they had overstepped, they might find themselves waltzing right out of office.

The train came to a stop. Seymour swung aboard. He waved good-by to Nielsen and the others who gave him a cheer as the locomotive gathered speed and soon disappeared in the night.

. . . *12*

DETECTIVES Tom Dusenberry, Phil Farley, John Eustace, and Sergeant John Young, dressed as laborers, were standing at the bar in a saloon with a sawdust sprinkled floor, liberally stained with tobacco juice. The crowded place was dingy, noisy, and ripe with the odors of stale tobacco, sweat, beer and an adjacent outhouse.

The saloon was located on First Avenue and 11th Street in the heart of "Mackerelville." In the slang of the day, a "mackerel" was a procurer—and there were plenty of them in Mackerelville, which ran from Second Avenue to the East River from 10th Street to 14th Street. Those few blocks contained more whores, pimps and madams than anyplace else in the city with the possible exception of Five Points or Paradise Square. The joints in Mackerelville were nothing like the fancy whorehouses

on Prince Street. No carriage trade came to these dives. Few
rounders with money dared venture into the neighborhood. Many
of Mackerelville's residents were criminals who thought nothing of knifing a man, stealing his watch, throwing his body into
the river, and then pawning the watch in one of the numerous
"lushing cribs" or pawnbroker-fence shops that studded the
vicinity.

Rioters drifted into Mackerelville by the hundreds and it became an unofficial assembly point for mobs rallying to attack
the downtown Negro sections and those along the west side.
Men armed with assorted weapons ran about. Carts had been
overturned and lashed together to form barricades which blocked
off First Avenue at 10th Street and at 14th Street. Smaller ob-
structions barred the cross streets. In large part, Mackerelville
became the headquarters of the rioters.

Young and his men were there because an informer had
tipped off the detectives that John Andrews was going to make
an appearance in the mob stronghold. Young had hurried down
to Mackerelville with his three colleagues in the hope of getting him.

The detectives remained quietly and inconspicuously at the
saloon bar listening to the drunken boasting of rioters who had
been out with mobs all day. The saloon grew so crowded that
customers had to stand in the doorway and out in the street
while friends passed steins of beer to them. Whores paraded the
sidewalks. Sharp-eyed pimps watched their girls and made note
of which ones landed a patron. Roving gangs shoved through
the crowds, heading downtown and carrying ropes and flaring
pine torches.

The detectives listened and marked those who boasted most
loudly of having helped to burn the Colored Orphan Asylum
or to loot Lexington Avenue brownstones. The detectives mem-
orized faces and names, but made no move to apprehend the
men. They were after bigger game—John Andrews. They would

trail him, get him alone and then arrest him. But there was, as yet, no sign of the man.

The bartender, who also happened to own the saloon, liked his customers to keep their glasses brimming. Any who did not were promptly thrown out by the apelike bouncer—a local rough named "Crusher." The bartender noticed that Young and his friends were doing no drinking. They were "cold turkeys" taking up room and not paying for it. He signaled for his strong-arm man, pointing out the detectives with an almost imperceptible nod.

Crusher plowed through the customers and pulled up in front of Young who happened to be standing nearest to him. The men faced each other for a moment, then recognition flared in Crusher's eyes. "Hey! It's Young!" the bruiser yelled. At the same instant, he lunged for the detective. Young ducked under his grip and drove his knee hard into Crusher's groin. As the man doubled up, the detective bashed him on the head with a heavy beer mug. Eustace, Farley and Dusenberry closed in around Young and hustled him out before any of the drink-clouded men in the place quite realized what had happened. Crusher writhed on the floor, blood pumping from his smashed head.

Not a single patron had any sympathy for him. Most could not contain their laughter at seeing the bouncer take a beating. Because of the noise in the saloon, very few had heard him denounce Young. If anyone had, he was keeping the information to himself. This was a good chance to get even with Crusher. Almost every man in the place had been roughed up by him at one time or another.

Somebody kicked him in the ribs—and chaos followed. Men pounded the groaning bruiser without mercy and after a while threw his battered hulk into a filthy, garbage-littered alleyway behind the saloon. They then turned on the bartender—a runt of a man with watery blue eyes and yellowed, snaggly teeth. They pitched him through the window of the saloon. He landed on the sidewalk, rolled into the gutter and lay still, torn and gashed by the glass.

His erstwhile customers then kicked in the door of the liquor storeroom. They grabbed up armloads of whisky bottles. For the fun of it, they stove in beer kegs and splashed around, ankle deep in the foaming brew.

A block from the saloon, Young held a council of war with his detectives. Since Andrews had not appeared, the mission was a failure, but Headquarters should be warned about the impending attacks on the Negro districts. Young decided he was the one to go back with the warning since he had been spotted once and might be recognized again if he remained, not only endangering himself, but the others, too.

An outburst of cheering attracted the attention of the detectives. A man was riding a horse down the sidewalk opposite them. The horseman was surrounded by enthusiastic admirers. Children darted in front of the horse and barely avoided being trampled upon.

"I'll be damned. It's Andrews. Will you look at him sitting that nag like he was a general," Young whispered.

Dusenberry reached into his pocket and partially drew his revolver. He was one of the best shots on the force. "Say the word, Young, and I'll finish the bastard now. We could slip into an alley and be away before they knew what was going on," he said.

"No, Tom. He's to be taken alive. You three stay with him. When you get a chance—take him!" Young ordered in a sharp tone.

The three detectives nodded and slipped into the jostling crowd which surrounded Andrews. Young watched for a moment as Andrews called to the eddying mob to head downtown toward the Negro districts on Thompson, Sullivan, Baxter, Clarkson and Carmine Streets. The rioters pushed against Young, carrying him along like a chip of wood on a wave. He managed to

slip off into a side street and hurried through the darkness to
Police Headquarters.

The mob had a ribald time on the way. Nearly everyone had
a bottle. Drunken women staggered along. Couples made love in
hallways. It was a big, wild spree, an unholy Mardi Gras. The
mob's motives and purposes seemed to have been forgotten in
the carnival-like revelry. But some of the rioters remembered.
This was going to be the biggest lynching party in history. Before they were through, every lamppost would be decorated with
a "nigger."

A good many in the mob had additional ideas. They felt the
Negroes could wait a bit. Lynching wasn't that much of a nov-
elty. First, another old score had to be settled. Almost every
rioter hated Horace Greeley, the sharp-penned editor of *The
Tribune*. He had blasted, insulted and scolded those he called
Copperheads, describing them as traitors or worse. His venom
was aimed at Democrats particularly. And he had even crossed
polemics with John Hughes, Archbishop of the Roman Catholic
Church in the New York Diocese. Greeley had written hard
words and many rioters decided this was the chance to get even
with him.

People started yelling, "Let the niggers wait! Let's get Greeley!
On to *The Tribune!* Hang Greeley!"

Hanging appealed to the rioters—the "niggers" or Greeley—
it didn't matter as long as there was to be hanging. They cheered
heartily at the idea. Hundreds started to sing to the tune of
"John Brown's Body":

> "We'll hang old Greeley to a sour apple tree,
> We'll hang old Greeley to a sour apple tree,
> We'll hang old Greeley to a sour apple tree,
> And send him straight to Hell!"

They moved off, singing and waving their flaring torches in
time to the music. Down Third Avenue they went, to the Bow-

ery, through Chatham Square and along Park Row—the identical route up which the ill-fated Invalid Corps platoon had marched in the morning.

Restive crowds had gathered in Park Row and the streets facing on City Hall Park. The snub-nosed howitzers and the ranks of infantry kept the rowdy assemblages from attempting a move against City Hall itself. As the uptown mob poured by on its way to Printing House Square and *The Tribune* building, these demonstrators eagerly swelled its numbers.

Fortunately for Greeley, someone warned him of the mob's intentions. The noted editor was far bolder with pen than sword and he fled ignominiously down the back stairs and into Anne Street where friends rushed him to Windust's restaurant. He remained hidden in the dining room under a table behind the folds of a damask cloth.

The mob, in the meantime, rushed the building, beat up the lone policeman on duty and tried to set the place afire while printers and editorial workers escaped by the same back stairway which Greeley had used.

The rioters shouted gleefully over what they thought was a victory. They had started a small blaze in *The Tribune* business office when a police detachment under Captain John Jourdan came charging across Printing House Square. The locust sticks sent the rioters fleeing toward the Park. The police stamped out the fire and set off in pursuit.

This mob ran into some very bad luck. Inspector Dan Carpenter and his riot smashers were on patrol nearby, reinforced by one hundred Brooklyn policemen under Inspector John Folk. Carpenter, in the front, as usual, spotted the fleeing rioters. He formed his men in a solid rank across the street, blocking the way. The rioters were trapped in a pincers movement as Carpenter and Folk's men charged them. Jourdan's detachment clubbed its way to Carpenter and Folk. It was an evening of good hunting for the police. The encounter, which had begun at

8:00 P.M, was ended by 8:15 P.M. The mob had been scattered into a thousand parts.

Jourdan detached fifty men to guard Printing House Square and Carpenter led his happy warriors back to Police Headquarters again. Folk went back to Brooklyn with his command and received an accolade from Mayor Kalbfleisch, himself.

The sheepish *Tribune* staff returned to the building determined not to be routed so ingloriously again. An enterprising policeman named Blackwell, who was attached to the Harbor Police, brought a load of pistols and carbines from the city stores on Ward's Island and distributed them to the *Tribune* people. Lanterns were hung out to illuminate the street below and with sentries stationed at the windows, the members of the fourth estate went back to the business of putting out a newspaper.

Greeley escaped with ruffled dignity. He crawled out of his inglorious refuge and stormed into his office where he scribbled an hysterical editorial for the next edition. At 10:00 P.M. another, smaller mob, ignorant of the fate suffered by the first, tried to attack the building a second time. This onslaught was routed in a few minutes by the police in the Square and trigger-happy *Tribune* staffers who whanged away with much ardor but poor marksmanship, proving to be more of a menace to public safety than the mob.

13

THE mob poured into the Negro district, and one part of it headed for Clarkson Street. Despite all the disorders the Negro neighborhoods had not yet borne the full brunt of the mob's fury.

Like other streets in the 8th Ward, Clarkson Street was an area of dilapidated shacks and wooden tenements. Whole families occupied cellars in this overpopulated section, and after heavy rains, these basement apartments became flooded, and stinking, stagnant water lingered continually. In the summer, flies, carrying diseases bred in the garbage heaps and fetid outhouses, swarmed everywhere. Stench and putrescence blighted the lives of everyone on Clarkson Street. The children grew to repeat the pattern of misery.

There was never real quiet on Clarkson Street. It was always noisy—shouts, curses, music, laughter. On this hot night hundreds of children scampered about playing among refuse piles in which fat gray rats burrowed.

The quiet, gentle-eyed, soft-spoken Negro seated in the creaking rocker in a three-room shack on Clarkson Street was a longshoreman named William Jones. It was an odd coincidence that the first man drafted on Saturday had borne the same name. The Negro was a spare, bent man with sunken cheeks, frizzled gray hair and a hacking cough which sometimes made him spit up blood.

His wife was only forty years old but seemed much older. She was a kitchen maid in a rich man's brownstone on Stuyvesant Square. For this work she was paid fifty cents a day. As she moved about putting the supper dishes away, she limped from a rheumatic twinge in her right knee.

Her chores completed, she sat down facing William. He

smiled and said, "How about a walk, Mary? There'll be some air down by the river."

She massaged the sore knee gently. "I've got the misery, Will. I believe it's fixin' to rain."

"That misery of yours is better'n a barometer. When does it tell you we'll have the rain?" he laughed.

"Late this night," she said positively.

He reached for his pipe and a packet of coarse tobacco. "I've got time for a walk then. You won't mind if I go to the river for a spell?"

"You know I don't mind. While you're out, fetch a loaf of bread from Perry's. Git it before your walk or he'll be closed when you git back. Don't stay late."

He rose and stretched his thin arms. "I'll be home early. Work day tomorrow. Figure I've lazed enough, not goin' to the shape-up all last week."

"Lazed! Will, you know you've been sick with that cough——"

"I should've gone to work, anyway."

"A fine lot of good you'd have been, like you was—weak as a baby."

Weak as a baby, he thought. He was a feeble old man, now.

He shook his head, remembering the time he had been young and strong and supple. Then he had been first on the docks at the daily shape-up, the only Negro the hiring bosses picked before a white man. He remembered and sighed as he lit his pipe and left the shack. Clarkson Street teemed with life.

People sat on stoops, leaned against sagging picket fences or squatted along the curbstones. A passer-by had to pick his way through the crowds blocking the walks. Someone was strumming a banjo and the player was surrounded by a swaying, hand clapping throng. These shacks on Clarkson Street could have been slave cabins on a plantation in the deep South. These were the sounds and voices and songs.

William strolled by the loungers, nodding and exchanging

greetings. He paused to chat with a few men and the talk was about the trouble in the city. Some showed fear, some blustered, and some pretended indifference, each meeting fear in his own way. William listened and prayed inwardly that there would be no violence on Clarkson Street. He tried to make himself believe that the mob wasn't coming because it had not yet been there.

He walked to the bakery at the bottom of the street and bought a loaf of bread. Outside the small bakeshop he sniffed the loaf, and the aroma reminded him of long ago in the little cabin on the upstate farm, and his mother baking bread and the wonderful smells that came from the brick oven and the taste of the bread, freshly baked. Although he had been away for so many years, he still recalled details of his life on the farm. He saw the little farm in the spring with the new green shoots coming up out of the rain-drenched brown earth, and the way it had been in the winter when the brittle, frozen snow crackled as you stepped on it. He remembered the sound. Snap. Snap. Snap. . . .

And he was hearing that sound now. Snap. Snap. Snap. He looked around, startled. He heard the sound once more. Snap. Snap.

Briefly there was silence . . . then a confusion of yelling and screaming. This uproar came from far down Clarkson Street, hidden in a darkness spotted with pale lamplight from the windows of the shacks and the feeble glow of widely scattered street lamps.

William stared into the dark, trembling with apprehension. He decided that a brawl had broken out on the street. Such frays were common enough. He heard the snapping sound again and this time he recognized it. Revolver shots. Some drink-crazed black man had gone berserk. Clarkson Street was well acquainted with the flash of a razor, the crack of a pistol, and the sprawled body in the gutter after the flare-up of violence.

The yells grew louder and as William watched, a streak of

orange-hued fire shot up into the night. William gasped. Fire was dreaded on Clarkson Street. The rotten, dried out wooden shacks and tenements were highly inflammable. Fire could sweep that block in minutes. He started to run, slipping a bit in the soft earth of the mud flats. After a few yards he had to stop when a fit of coughing overtook him. He bent double, ruckling and spitting blood. He recovered in a few moments and lumbered awkwardly in stiff-legged strides, still carrying the loaf of bread. He reached the walk on the street near the bakery. Rows of shacks were ablaze and the flames caught on from one building to another.

Before he could move, a band of white men rushed at him. They struck him with clubs, and the loaf of bread fell to the ground where it was trampled into pulp. Feebly, William tried to fight back, but they struck him down again and stomped on him with heavy boots. They threw a rope around him and dragged his body in the gutter. They hanged him to a tree at the entrance of St. John's Cemetery and gibbering women came to slash at his corpse with knives. They splashed kerosene on his clothes and set him afire.

The flames from the shacks joined in a huge bonfire. Rioters danced in dizzy circles, faces red, mouths agape. Children had tagged along with the mob. They stood fascinated and watched William's body shrivel as it burned.

14

THE Mayor sat huddled in a chair against a basement wall of Police Headquarters, a dead cigar clenched between his teeth. His face was ashen; in the space of a few hours he had lost his air of patrician arrogance. Anyone seeing him for the first time would have mistaken him for a sagging and aging clerk rather than the mayor of the nation's largest city.

He sat staring at the floor, speaking to no one, bowed with the shock of what had happened to his snug world. The rioters had violated his complacent sanctuary. They had attacked his home and destroyed the gun factory.

He looked around with dead eyes. Men were hurrying about the huge room. Soldiers trailing muskets trotted in. Officers strutted back and forth, their sabers knocking against the furniture. Calm policemen inspected revolvers. The telegraph keys kept up their interminable clatter.

Acton was standing at a long table bending over a map and listening to a young army liuetenant—a boy barely old enough to shave—who was pointing to a spot on the map. General Brown joined them. The lieutenant finished his report, saluted Brown and trotted out.

Opdyke had worked hard and long to attain his present position. He was the Mayor—and now the lazy rabble, the sweepings of the slum gutters, was trying to destroy him. He thought about those people. They moaned about poverty but did nothing to escape from it except to get drunk. The Mayor had been poor, too. But he had worked, and worked hard. At sixteen he was teaching school in Hunterdon County, New Jersey. But that wasn't enough for him. He didn't intend to spend his whole life instructing cloddish farm boys. After two years he was clerk-

ing in a downtown store near the Battery, and at twenty-seven
he had opened the first clothing factory in New York City.

He had made a gentleman of himself—but that didn't mean
he no longer knew how to fight. No matter what happened to
him, the mob was going to be smashed, and if it came to taking
a club or a gun and going out into the streets himself, he'd show
everyone that the Mayor of New York City did not lack courage.

He relit his cigar, stood up, tall and imposing, and went to
take his place beside Acton and Brown. . . .

The reports were unfavorable. The mob was everywhere, like
a hydra. Acton wondered how it had managed to spread so
swiftly. The rioters had destroyed twelve buildings on Broadway
between 28th and 29th Streets. Postmaster Abram Wakeham's
gracious home on East 87th Street had been gutted by fire. The
mob had also burned Provost Marshal Robert Nugent's house in
Yorkville. It had made no difference to the rioters that Nugent
once had been Colonel of the 69th Regiment—the "Fighting
Irish." And in addition to all this destruction, the station house of
the 23rd Precinct had been put to the torch.

Men constantly stumbled into Headquarters to bring word
of unbelievable brutalities committed by the mobs. Small police
details were overwhelmed, the officers mercilessly beaten. To
Acton the picture was black. And then, at the lowest ebb, he received this telegram:

> For Commissioner Acton:
> Mob everywhere. In all the streets. Shall we shut up shop?
> Cameron, 18th Precinct.

Acton shut his eyes for a moment and visualized the 18th
Precinct building, a two-story red brick affair on East 22nd
Street. Men from the 18th had defended the State Armory.
Cameron ran a good "shop" as he called it. His men were among
the best on the force. Acton knew if he gave the order to fight,
Cameron would carry it out to the death. It was not possible for

him to give such an order. He could not sacrifice those men. He dispatched a wire:

> 18th Precinct from Acton:
> Close shop. Report to Central Office.
>   Acton.

Everywhere, the mob. It controlled the streets. No one was safe. Reports poured in with details of robberies, muggings, lootings and murder:

Joseph Reed, seven years old, Negro, beaten to death with pistol butts by a band of white men.

Joseph Jackson, nineteen, Negro, an illiterate cowherd, he had been gathering provender for his herd stockaded at the foot of East 34th Street. A band of roughs threw him into the river and stoned him to death as he struggled in the water.

Everywhere, the mob. And everywhere darkness except for a few bright spots such as Carpenter's victories on Broadway and at *The Tribune,* and the rout of the mob at the State Armory.

There were other small triumphs:

A man named John Stephenson who owned a machine foundry on East 27th Street formed his workers into a shock troop and routed the mob that was trying to close all the shops in the vicinity. A dour Scotsman, John Stephenson was not one to be ordered about by anybody, much less a crowd of rioters. He was a Highland giant with the spirit of an eagle.

A committee from the mob pushed into his office. Stephenson listened to their demands—that he close his factory or suffer the consequences of having his shop burned down. When the spokesman was finished with his threat, Stephenson picked the man up in his great hands and pitched him into the street. He turned on the rest of the six-man committee, who were lucky to escape with bloodied noses, smashed jaws and missing teeth.

Stephenson put the question to his workers. If they chose to go it was their privilege. Any who wanted to stay would have to fight. Not a man moved to leave and when the rioters returned en masse Stephenson and his workers were ready for them. The battle was brief. The rioters, those who were able, managed to crawl away.

At nightfall, the workers volunteered to guard the premises. Stephenson supplied them with food and whisky. He got them firearms as well, and hung up a boldly lettered sign advising that anyone who attempted to interfere with the operation of his factory would be considered a trespasser and shot on sight. Not a single rioter dared venture near Stephenson's factory.

Tompkins Square was a German neighborhood, the residents being mainly veterans who had fought on the barricades in '48 during the democratic uprisings in Central Europe. Loyal Unionists almost to the man, the inhabitants of Tompkins Square armed themselves, and about a thousand of them patrolled the streets of their own neighborhood. Acton was told it would not be necessary to send either police or soldiers to Tompkins Square. If any rioters showed up they would be taken care of promptly.

Acton could see, from the windows of Police Headquarters, the glare of unchecked fires. He felt hemmed in by disaster. He saw it in the flames. They were all doomed and the great city was doomed with them. . . . He struggled against this feeling of hopelessness. The fight had only been joined. If the mobs were to win it could never be said it was because Tom Acton had shirked his duty. He turned wearily as a telegrapher handed him another batch of wires, and began to read. . . .

Men of the New York regiments bivouacked near Gettysburg lounged at campfires, smoking pipes, cleaning equipment, boiling up coffee, and talking about the recent battle. They were not yet aware of what was happening in New York City.

Nor could they know that the cumbersome machinery of the War Department was turning. Couriers had galloped out into the night. Messages were making the telegraph wires hum, and busy adjutants were writing the orders that would send the New Yorkers rushing back to the metropolis—not to be welcomed by cheers and kisses—but to help wrest the city from the hands of enemies they had once called neighbors.

Ross Lane studied a map of the city. His pale face was haggard and dirty stubble showed on his chin. His clothes were soiled and the finger which moved about on the map was dirty. Disappointment rankled in him. Others might be gloating, but as far as he was concerned the uprising was a complete failure. Not a single important objective had been taken. The Copperheads had not swarmed into action; only a drunken rabble had joined the battle.

He glanced about at the men in the room, making them out in the wan light of the lamps. Some were his own exhausted men who had been on the go since early morning. A frightened looking John Andrews was there—subdued and quiet, nothing like the bombastic orator of Third Avenue. A man—supposedly a representative of Ben and Fernando Wood—stood in a corner frowning churlishly. A few Five Points gang leaders were present—and that was it. Nobody of any account. No army officers coming over with their troops. No dedicated revolutionaries. Not one dependable man except his own people.

Suddenly a shudder went through Lane. He felt that soon he would be dead. Tomorrow, Ross Lane, Captain, C.S.A., would die on a hostile street of an alien city far from the gentle greensward of Virginia.

He shook off the icy dread, and tapped the map with his forefinger. The men gathered closer around him. "We must do it here. We've got to capture the Union Steam Works and the weapons stored within the place. We failed at the armory—but we must not fail here," he said.

The men nodded. Tomorrow. The Union Steam Works. An

ugly red brick building one block north of the State Armory. It was a pipe and tubing factory now turning out guns. Thousands of weapons were stored there. It was a prime target. There was really nothing to it. The agitators would go out and tell the shanty dwellers that Lincoln meant to give young colleens to the free niggers. Tell them anything. Feed them enough whisky and they'd storm the sky.

The Union Steam Works. Tomorrow.

Captain Ross Lane smiled. Not many had his good fortune. He knew precisely where he was going to die.

At 11:00 P.M. it rained. A cloudburst beat down on the city and drowned the fires. The downpour emptied the streets of rioters. Some claimed the storm had saved New York from destruction. The city had been spared from the flames only to face an even greater ordeal during the forthcoming day.

Tuesday
July 14, 1863

. . . *1*

THE violence that had been born in the city and spread to the outskirts reversed its pattern on Tuesday morning. The city was quiet. No cars rolled along the street railways. The big streetcars stood forlornly in the depots and the horses stamped impatiently in their stalls. This morning there would be no bag of oats at dawn, no bustle in the stableyards, and bridle straps creaking in the early light.

Silence hung over the city—brooding and alien. Tuesday dawned hot. The sun was a red fireball in the cloudless sky. Steam rose from rain-wet sidewalks. The roadways were dotted with puddles. The city seemed like a deserted place. Ferry slips were empty and no boats were running. Factories were idle, fires had turned cold in furnaces, the chimneys were smokeless.

During the night wary skippers of merchant ships that had been tied up at piers hauled anchor and moved out to the mouth of the Bay. The docks and water front had no sign of life. But if the city was in the grip of paralysis, the evil that had churned it into upheaval the day before flared afresh in the suburbs. In the rustic villages of Yorkville and Harlem, crowds swirled about looting shops, burning houses and overturning vehicles. The Mott Haven trestle bridge was destroyed. Wagons carrying produce from Westchester County farms and heading toward the New York City markets were ambushed by ragged bands of men and boys. Homes were plundered. Rioters beat householders, and the quiet, isolated reaches of the city became places of utter terror.

Howling rowdies had paraded the streets all night. And as the darkness waned, men peered from behind shuttered windows and recognized the frenzied faces of townsmen in the mob. Those in the streets had ripped away the mask. Greed and hatred and envy goaded them on. This was their opportunity to strike against more prosperous neighbors and they seized it. The riot gave them license and they were using it to loot and burn.

It was a mob of handymen and porters, street sweepers and dustmen, lamplighters, chimney cleaners and carters—the people who served the rich and lived in rotting shanties and moldering frame houses. But in the midst of these dispossessed were strangers, men who pointed and directed, led and controlled. They were the men who studied and understood the maps on which were marked bridges and railroads—telegraph lines and gas works.

And early on Tuesday morning the riot which had ebbed for the moment in the city, flourished in the hinterlands.

And then, as a plague feeds on itself, the pestilence turned back on the metropolis. But before it was spent in Yorkville, a mob had burned the police station and used flaming pieces of the building as firebrands to set other blazes.

As the fires were spreading in Yorkville and in Harlem, fast riding messengers brought the bad news to military headquarters where dyspeptic old General Wool sipped his customary morning cup of hot lemon juice and fretted at his desk. He sent a petulant telegram to General Brown at Police Headquarters:

HEADQUARTERS DEPARTMENT OF THE EAST
New York City, July 14, 1863

TO: BRIGADIER GENERAL HARVEY BROWN, U.S.A.

Sir:

It is reported that the rioters have already recommenced their work of destruction. Today there must be no child's play. Some of the troops under your command should be sent immediately to attack and stop those who have begun their infernal rascality in Yorkville and Harlem.

John E. Wool
Major-General

At Police Headquarters there was great activity. Hastily formed military detachments stood under arms in marching gear. General Brown conferred with his officers. Police Commissioner Acton had stayed on duty all through the night. Red-eyed and tired, he was still checking reports and organizing his men into striking units. By Tuesday morning, every available policeman had been mobilized for duty. Several hundred were assembled at Headquarters, and the streets around the building were an armed military encampment.

The troubles in Yorkville and Harlem had to be ignored, for detectives began filtering in with accounts of huge crowds collecting throughout the city as on the previous day.

And, like belated heralds, the newspapers came out with bold headlines telling everyone what they already knew, that a terrible riot was wracking the city.

The temper of the editors was summed up in a front page editorial which appeared in the *New York Post*:

"Let the artillery give the rioters an abundance of grape and canister and that at once. The danger is too great to trifle with. . . ."

At a very early hour, Governor Seymour had arrived in the city. A squad of soldiers met him at the Jersey City terminal and escorted him to the St. Nicholas Hotel where an opulent suite was converted into an office for the Governor. Mayor Opdyke joined him there, accompanied by other city officials.

Without stopping to refresh himself, Seymour went into conference with the Mayor. All political considerations were laid aside in the interest of the city and the public safety. Immediately after this meeting, Seymour issued a proclamation. It stated, in part:

The laws of the State of New York must be enforced, peace and order maintained and the lives and property of all its citizens protected at any and every hazard. I therefore call upon all persons engaged in these riotous proceedings to retire to their homes and employments, declaring that unless they do so at once, I shall use all the power necessary to restore the peace and the order of the city.

Horatio Seymour, Governor

The city was placarded with this warning from the Governor and a proclamation by Mayor Opdyke which ordered all persons who sold arms and ammunition to close their places of business. Since the mobs had looted almost every gunshop in the city, Mayor Opdyke was actually issuing an empty manifesto.

Newspapers carried appeals from military units which had served out their enlistments, urging members to assist in putting down the disorders. For example:

National Zouaves! Attention! The officers and members of the 10th Regiment, New York Volunteers who are willing to assist in the enforcement of the laws are requested to meet at 525 Broadway, Armory of the 37th New York State Guards, as early this day as possible, in full uniform.

John E. Bendix, Colonel

A plea for citizens to volunteer as special deputies for the duration of the riot went out and special meetings were held in various parts of the city to form neighborhood defense organizations. And while all this was happening, the growling voices of mobs were heard with ever-increasing menace. The pressure was rising and somewhere a major outbreak was in the making. No one, except those who had laid the plans, knew precisely where it would come. . . .

A Negro shoemaker named James Costello, who lived at 97 West 33rd Street, went into the street early in the morning to buy some medicine for his youngest child who had the whooping cough. He knew the dangers he faced, but the child needed the syrup.

Costello owned an old dragoon pistol. It was rusty and had not been fired for years, but he loaded the weapon, thrust it into his belt and hurried off on the errand. Neighborhood roughs spotted the Negro and took out after him, hallooing and shouting like hunting dogs after a fox.

A man named Thomas Maney caught up with Costello and started to beat him with a club. The desperate Negro drew his pistol and pulled the trigger. The ancient weapon went off with an echo-wakening explosion. Maney dropped to the sidewalk with a gaping wound in his chest.

Costello tried to get away, but there was no escape for him. Maney's friends closed in, dragged the Negro to the roof of a nearby building and hurled the screaming man into the street.

Negroes fled to the police stations. They came as refugees fleeing from an overwhelming disaster. Young mothers carried babies. Old women hobbled on painful feet, backs bent under the burden of small pitiful treasures which were trash to all but the poor. Each had saved some special belonging—a feather pillow, a blanket, a pair of shoes, a trinket. To the old and the poor these were priceless things. The brick station buildings with the flickering green-shaded gas lamps outside were sanctuaries for the Negroes. The big, mustached white men in the blue, brass-buttoned uniforms would protect them, they believed.

As the news of the rioting swept through the Negro sections, many could not believe the terror would really come to them. They were reluctant to leave the places in which they lived. No matter the unpainted walls, the rotting floors, the leaking roofs. No matter the sagging beds, the foul outhouses, the stench-filled hallways. The festering streets were familiar havens and the stinking tenements were homes.

And because this was so they were reluctant to leave although those who came with the alarm had seen the terror and described what they had seen. Young men listened with bowed heads and knotted fists, anger drumming in their veins. They were descendants of African warriors, with strong black faces and clear eyes, who had been driven to sweeping streets, cleaning spittoons and emptying swill cans. Anger rose in them like burning poison. They yearned for a chance to strike a blow at the rioters. They were the ones whose backs had been scarred by the lash, who had fled through swamp and forest, hiding in cellars and barns of the underground railroad, living on roots and bark to escape slavery. They were without fear. But now they abandoned their possessions, and to protect their families, fled with them to the police stations.

In one precinct, the Sixth, located at Franklin and Baxter Streets on the edge of the Negro quarter, several hundred colored persons gathered. They sat on the floor, squatted in corners, slumped on benches. The desk sergeant's beefy face was creased with anxiety. His worry spread to the Negroes, and their uneasy whispers were like breezes soughing furtively in a forest.

They could hear what was happening in the streets around the station house—the hoarse shouting and the sounds of breaking glass. A policeman staggered into the station house, his face bloody, his uniform blouse ripped. He had lost his hat and his stick, but clutched a drawn revolver. He cried out, "Sergeant! For God's sake, the mob's coming to burn the station house. We can't stop 'em. Get these people out of here!"

A frightened cry went up from the Negroes. An old woman

dropped to her knees and prayed in a wailing voice. A young girl clutched her baby and cried, "No! No! No!" The sergeant tugged at his drooping mustache and tried to avoid the eyes that were turned on him. His palms were damp with sweat and the high, tight collar of his blouse felt like a noose. He gripped the edge of his desk with nervous fingers. The precinct house was in his charge. He knew what mobs were and the effects of hatred and whisky. If he turned these Negroes loose, there would be lynchings. Yet, he could not protect them for the station house was no longer safe.

He pounded his fist on the desk. "Damn it! I need men. Give me twenty good lads and I'd send that rabble back to their holes. What can I do?" He spoke to the Negroes as though appealing to them for understanding.

A muscular young Negro pushed his way to the desk from the back of the room. "You can have all the men you need, Sergeant. We can fight. You've got clubs and revolvers. We can use them. Give us a chance for our lives. That's the least you can do."

The Sergeant and the Negro looked into each other's eyes. The officer knew this black man was right. He liked the Negroes of his precinct. They were sober and hard-working people. But the very thought of arming Negroes frightened him. He had waited years to get his sergeancy and he did not know how it would sit with his superiors if he issued arms to these people. Still, they were going to enlist blacks in the army, and teaching them to kill rebs wasn't any different than letting them fight that mob outside. What were they anyway but a pack of rebels, Copperheads, draft-dodging, traitorous bastards? If it was legal for blacks to fight on a battlefield, why not here? Besides, there was no other hope of saving the station house. He could scarcely sit here and play God with the lives of innocent people without giving them the chance he would afford to a dog.

And they were not dogs. They were human beings who loved and prayed to the same God he did, who knew pain and hunger, and fear. He hesitated only a moment, before taking a ring of keys from his desk drawer.

"All right. I'll swear in any man as temporary deputy to defend public property. Line up to receive your arms!" he said.

He went to the big arms chest standing in the back of the room and unlocked it.

When the mob finally came there were forty armed Negroes standing shoulder-to-shoulder in front of the building. Others manned the windows. The black men gripped their locust sticks firmly. The mob came on and when the rioters saw the black phalanx the ringleaders called a halt. They knew the Negroes would die fighting and being a mob they backed off shouting and cursing, afraid of the Negroes and their retribution.

The mob retreated and turned to do its work in other places and the street resumed its usual serenity. The houses stood as they had, with neat wrought-iron fences surrounding tidy front yards.

It was a street of frame houses with green shutters where children could play and peddlers came to sell country grown vegetables from wagons. The street bordered the scabrous Negro section but seemed divorced from it by an unbridgeable chasm. And, as it had survived the weather of the years, the births and the deaths, the street resumed its tranquillity. It seemed unchanged except for scattered mementos of the invasion: trampled grass on front lawns, torn paper, some windows broken, empty whisky bottles, and a raggedy shirt that had been thrown away by its wearer.

Yet, there had been a subtle change. It had come when the fingers of a black man curled around the stock of a pistol or touched the polished smoothness of a locust stick. The men who had actually faced the mob with stick and gun remained at their posts with quiet assurance. Nothing would ever be quite the same for them. They had experienced the feeling of dignity and self-respect which only free men have.

THE mob poured into Second Avenue. Though some carried muskets and pistols, the bulk was armed with an assortment of makeshift weapons. From 13th Street, the mob stretched northward to 33rd Street. It swarmed around the Union Steam Works on 22nd Street, and people rummaged around in the skeletonized blackened ruins of the State Armory a block to the south. Rioters clustered about the massive iron doors of the Steam Works and pounded on them with musket butts and clubs. The blows echoed hollowly. As the doors resisted, interest started to wane among the members of the mob. A gang had ransacked nearby saloons and men distributed bottles of whisky. Soon the drinking became widespread and whole crowds were staggering about, stupid with liquor.

Ross Lane, dressed in the soiled working clothes he had worn since Monday, went from group to group trying to keep the attention of the rioters turned to smashing in the doors. Looking at him, no one would believe he was an officer. His unshaven face was streaked with grime. The heavy work shoes he wore were shapeless and scuffed. His flannel shirt was rumpled and the blue denim trousers were stained. But beneath these clothes he was wearing fine linen undergarments, and in his pocket he carried the ornately engraved gold watch that had been his father's.

Within the watch case was a miniature of his family. His father, mother, and two sisters were stiffly posed for the daguerreotype. Now he had no time to think of them or the Virginia mansion with its rolling ground that sloped gently to the riverbank. The house was a ruin with only the chimney remaining

Courtesy New-York Historical Society, New York City

Enraged rioters, led by women, brutally stoned Colonel H. F. O'Brien to death in the vicinity of his home at 34th Street near Second Avenue.

Courtesy New-York Historical Society, New York City

Shortly after the rioting flared up on Third Avenue and 46th Street, the mob was harangued by its organizer, John U. Andrews.

Courtesy New-York Historical Society, New York City

Children romped about the body of a soldier killed in a fight on East Side.

The Negro quarter on Sullivan Street was under constant attack by rioters.

Courtesy New-York Historical Society, New York City

Bands of men roamed the streets to find Negroes and beat them, many fatally.

Women rioters led in looting of homes and spurred men on to acts of violence.

Courtesy New-York Historical Society, New York City

One of the mob's first acts was to loot and destroy the Colored Orphan Asylum located on Fifth Avenue between 45th and 46th Streets.

Courtesy New-York Historical Society, New York City

The fashionable Brooks Brothers clothing store at Catherine and Ann Streets was raided and ransacked by rioters on the night of July 14th.

Courtesy New-York Historical Society, New York City

First Avenue was the scene of bloody clashes between rioters and troops. The soldiers, on several occasions, used artillery to break up the mobs.

On July 13th, police led by Inspector Dan Carpenter crushed a huge mo

Courtesy New-York Historical Society, New York City

Cannon kept rioters from The Arsenal on Seventh Avenue and 35th Street.

Courtesy New-York Historical Society, New York City

dway between Bond and Amity Streets. It was the first victory for police.

Courtesy New-York Historical Society, New York City

Rioters tried to burn the Tribune Building four times because the paper, edited by Horace Greeley, favored the draft. Police smashed each attack.

Courtesy New-York Historical Society, New York City

Innocent Negroes, regardless of age were hunted and pursued by the mob. Many were trapped in the empty lots that dotted the Lexington Avenue area.

Courtesy New-York Historical Society, New York City

Almost at once, the rioters turned to looting and plunder. Wild mobs surged along Lexington Avenue, ransacking the wealthy brownstones in a display of senseless pillaging. For hours, during the early part of Monday, July 13th, the mob raged about completely uncontrolled.

Culver Service

Inspector Daniel C. Carpenter

Culver Service

Mayor George Opdyke

Culver Service

Major General John E. Wool

Culver Service

Police Commissioner Thomas C. Acton

like a bleak, lonely sentry guarding the rubble. The war had rolled by, swept back and come again. His father had been killed at Antietam, sword in hand, leading his regiment in a futile charge up the Bloody Lane. His mother was far off in Alabama with the girls and he was here, in New York City, caught up in a screaming, drunken mob, trying to make city scum behave like soldiers.

His own men were formed in a compact group. Every available squad had been assembled so that more than a hundred of them stood together, ready for action. They were dressed like the most ordinary workingman in the mob, coarse clothing, heavy shoes, floppy, battered hats. But despite their appearance no one could mistake them for part of the mob.

Anger grew in Ross as he moved among the rioters. He watched them drinking and fighting each other for whisky, and felt both a sense of disgust and mounting betrayal. This scum had done nothing except burn a few buildings and kill innocent Negroes. At the State Armory and on Broadway, a handful of disciplined policemen had scattered them. He watched a bearded fellow drain half a bottle of whisky, the liquor spilling over his beard and soaking his shirt. He symbolized to Ross the debased brutishness of the mob. Ross grabbed the bottle from the man's hand and smashed it on the sidewalk.

The rioter looked at him, startled, then with a snarl, the man yanked a knife from his belt. Ross whipped out his pistol and smashed the man across the face with the barrel. The rioter dropped to his knees, hands pressed against his ruined face, blood running between his fingers.

Facing the others, Ross cried, "You lousy gutter rats! Drink your bellies full, but not until we get the guns in that building!" He pointed to the Union Steam Works.

"Go get 'em, sonny," a man laughed, "we don't want 'em!"

"And who the hell do you think you might be?" another shouted.

"Listen to that Southern voice, will you? He's a skedaddler from Lee's army," a man cried.

They were closing in on Ross, circling, moving. The man he had struck uncovered his red-masked face. "Kick the shit out of him for me, boys," he pleaded.

Ross leveled his revolver. "I'll kill the first one who tries to touch me, and I mean it," he said.

The men glanced uneasily from one to the other. Suddenly, a way was forced through the crowd that surrounded Ross. A wedge of twenty men, led by a tall sunburned giant, broke through, with muskets at the port position and fingers curled lightly around the triggers. The leader stepped to Ross's side. "Thought you might like company, Captain," he said grinning.

Ross slipped his pistol back into a pocket. "Thanks, Gordon," he said.

The men formed a cordon around him and pushed out of the mob. The rioters scowled after Ross and the men with him.

"Did you see that?" one man said. "They called him Captain. You know what I think——?"

"Nobody gives a damn, Donovan. Let's go find us a bottle."

"That eager son of a bitch wants to be a hero, it ain't no skin off our asses," another man said.

The rioters moved away, forgetting the injured man who dragged himself to the curbstone and sat there, head in hand, watching his blood drip into the gutter.

Chief Clerk Seth Hawley was an efficient man and did not get rattled in any emergency. Despite the confusion in Police Headquarters—the movements of troops and police, the influx of frightened Negroes, the injured being treated by hard-working doctors, the endless messages deluging the wires—Hawley fulfilled his duties with precise calm.

During the night, he had been assigned to assemble a fleet of lorries to transport a striking force quickly into a trouble zone.

Hawley had carried out that mission and now thirty lorries, each drawn by a team, were parked in a long line on the Mott Street side of the building. Policemen drivers held the reins and either a soldier or an armed special deputy was perched beside each one.

The lorry drivers did not have to wait long for their passengers. No sooner had the first attempt been made to storm the Union Steam Works than word flashed in from the 18th Precinct. Captain Cameron had closed his shop according to instructions, but four officers had volunteered to remain in the building as a safeguard. One of these men was a telegrapher. A glance out the shuttered window at the mob eddying around the Union Steam Works had been enough for him. He and his companions knew they could no longer stay in the building—but they delayed evacuation long enough to send this telegram:

18th Precinct to Central Office:
Mob everywhere trying to force entrance into Union Steam Works. Guns stored there. Come quickly. We must leave. Will try to reach Central Office in civilian dress. Come quickly in force.

When he received this, Acton sent for Inspector Carpenter whose detachment was standing by ready for instant action. Acton told him of the situation.

"You'll attack and disperse them, Inspector," Acton said.

"That I will," Carpenter said.

"I want a word with the boys," Acton said.

He followed Carpenter to the courtyard where the Inspector's men were waiting. Acton signaled for silence and spoke quietly to the men. "I would like to thank you for the work you have done. You have rendered the city of New York great and signal service and I assure you that your labors will not be forgotten."

When Acton had finished his short speech he turned to Carpenter and said, "It's up to you and these brave men, Inspector."

"We'll not fail, sir," Carpenter said. His eyes met Acton's for a moment. "If you don't mind, sir, I'll be asking a favor of you."

"Anything at all," Acton said.

"Sir, will you send word to Mrs. Carpenter that I am all right. She'll be that worried."

"I'll see to it personally, Dan," the Commissioner said. "Take care of yourself."

"That I will," Carpenter said gravely. He called to his men. "Into the lorries, lads."

The policemen ran for the vehicles, scrambling aboard in a matter of seconds. Carpenter gave the signal and the wagons rolled away with their loads of police cheering and waving their sticks in response to the shouts of soldiers and civilians in the streets around the Headquarters.

At the same time, as General Brown strode nervously about, a young captain assembled troops from Company H, 12th U.S. Infantry, and several companies of the 11th New York Volunteers reinforced by two pieces of artillery. This strong force was to follow up behind the police.

While the troops were getting in to line, a beefy bearded volunteer colonel by the name of Henry F. O'Brien galloped up on a black horse and reined in near Brown.

He leaned down in his saddle and said, "General Wool's compliments. I'm to command the 11th New York."

Brown looked at him coldly. "Damn it, sir! Where did you learn military courtesy? Get off that horse and report properly!"

A titter of laughter rippled through the ranks of the enlisted men. This promised to be a real treat. The men of the 11th New York Volunteers knew O'Brien as a pompous, politically influential officer who had been commissioned through pull. O'Brien was a Republican and a leader in the 21st Ward, particularly in the neighborhood of 34th Street and Second Avenue where he lived. Unschooled as an officer, he was reckless in battle and arrogantly brave. Now, his florid cheeks grew mottled and he frowned at General Brown, but few men could outface the gelid stare of the old regular.

O'Brien dismounted, drew himself to attention and saluted Brown smartly. "Colonel O'Brien reporting as directed by Major General Wool, sir. He requests the command of the 11th New York be turned over to me."

Brown nodded. "That's better. Might make a decent officer out of you in a few years. Take your post, sir. You will follow the 12th U.S. at a five minute interval. Lieutenant Eagleson and the artillery will be attached to your command." Turning from O'Brien, the General pointed to the youthful captain who led Company H. "Move out, Captain Franklin," he ordered.

The Captain saluted, called his men to attention and marched them off at a smart pace, the drummer taking up the cadence beat. Silently fuming, O'Brien swung back into the saddle and Brown walked off without a backward glance at the angry officer.

Five minutes later, O'Brien started uptown with the 11th New York and two pieces of artillery.

Governor Seymour faced the group of men sitting about in the luxurious parlor of his St. Nicholas Hotel suite. It was an imposing assemblage. The Mayor was present, chewing on a cigar. He, too, had spent the night at the St. Nicholas, rather than return home. Leading politicians from both parties were there. The air hung thick with cigar smoke and the men were hoarse from the continuous arguing and quibbling that had been going on since early morning.

A waiter stationed by a large coffee urn dispensed cups of the brew. And at the far end of the room a buffet table stood laden with sandwiches. A portable bar had been set up and a white-jacketed bartender kept the glasses filled. The scene reminded Seymour of a dozen other rooms in which he had attended political caucuses.

But this was no mere meeting to decide on a candidate. The fate of a city, perhaps the entire nation depended on what they did. Some urged the Governor to declare martial law and let the army take over the city government. This faction wanted to suspend civil rights, and when sufficient troops had arrived, to treat the rioters without mercy. Drumhead court-martials. Firing squads. Public floggings.

Seymour was loathe to take such a step. It would be an admission that his administration had been unable to restore order. He believed in civil authority and was convinced that it remained for the leaders of city and state to end the outbreak rather than resort completely to the military.

Seymour was aware of the whispers going on about him: the Governor and his Democratic henchmen would not crack down on the rioters, but intended to hamstring opposition to the outbreak in order to embarrass Lincoln's government. The whisper had been put into writing by Horace Greeley in a scathing editorial that had appeared in the first edition of *The Tribune:*

"If we had a commanding General possessed of energy, a Governor thoroughly loyal, and a mayor not absolutely paralyzed by fear, these howling fiends, these emissaries and spies of the rebels would have been shot down yesterday. . . ."

Apparently, Greeley had forgotten his own inglorious conduct of the previous days.

The Governor refused to be pushed. The draft law was the cause of this outbreak. If he could reach the people who had trust in him and speak to them, the Governor was sure he could convince them to stop their lawlessness. He decided he would deliver an address at noon from the steps of the City Hall. A promise from him that serious efforts were underway to suspend the draft might go far to mollify the rioters.

For once, Opdyke agreed with the Governor. Nothing could be lost by allowing him to speak and much might be gained. He ordered handbills printed and distributed to publicize the Governor's speech and the meeting broke up. The politicians drifted from the room and only the Governor and Mayor remained. The harassed executives faced each other.

"I think we'd better go to City Hall, Mayor Opdyke," Seymour said, "I would like to work on my speech."

"Of course, sir. I'll order my carriage. We'll ride down to the Hall together."

The Mayor opened the door of the suite and spoke to a police officer stationed in the corridor. The man saluted and hurried downstairs. When Opdyke re-entered the room, he found Seymour standing by the window and looking down into the street three stories below. As the Mayor joined him, Seymour pointed to a dozen cavalrymen who surrounded a carriage parked at the entrance of the hotel.

"Is that an escort for us, Mr. Opdyke?" Seymour asked.

"General Brown thought it best."

Seymour turned from the window and smiled. "Generals think guns and sabers solve every problem."

He looked at Opdyke with a searching glance. "Mr. Opdyke, if you and I are forced to travel the short distance between this hotel and City Hall under the guard of armed horsemen we are admitting the rioters control the city."

"Yes, sir. What else can we do, though? We must get to City Hall."

"I have heard, Mr. Opdyke, customarily you walk to your office each morning, down Broadway."

"Yes, that's so."

"Then, sir, don't you think it would be a display of confidence and a great morale booster for the general public if you did not deviate from your usual practice this morning?"

Opdyke rolled the cigar in his mouth and regarded the Governor with amusement. "If you'll accompany me, Governor—I'll walk."

"Very well, Mr. Opdyke. It's a deal."

The men grinned at each other understandingly. There was no rift between them now. Actually, they were quite alike in certain ways. Both were big men, over six feet tall, in the prime of life and health. Each in his own way had learned never to give up without a fight. Seymour came from an old American family; he was not a self-made man in the sense of the mayor. His father had been a successful merchant in upstate New York and he had not had to struggle for his advantages. Nevertheless he had always been a fighter for the things he believed in. If Seymour had any great fault it was his faith in intellect and logic even in situations which called for direct action and force.

Opdyke agreed to walk to City Hall because it was good politics. The citizens who saw him would remember his courage. But he had no intention of dismissing the cavalry escort. A quiet word to the troop commander would keep the horsemen within easy range. Opdyke ran no unnecessary personal risks any more than he took risky business chances.

Shortly after, the Mayor and the Governor were leisurely strolling down Broadway. Occasionally, a vehicle rolled along, but only at a fast pace. In the dozen or so blocks between the St. Nicholas Hotel and City Hall, they met only a few people hurrying along with heads bent. But from the shelter of the closed windows, hundreds watched them and the sight of the chief executives walking with apparent casualness was an encouraging one. Perhaps, the onlookers thought, the trouble was over; it certainly appeared that it was, with no signs of rioters downtown. As a result, people began drifting into the street from various hiding places and a vestige of familiarity returned to Broadway. Men gathered outside hotels and saloons to talk over the events. Even a few sidewalk vendors nervously crying their wares put in an appearance. Traffic began to flow gradually, although no public conveyances moved.

Here and there a shop opened, the metal shutters grating as they were rolled up. Awnings were lowered against the morning sun. Postmen ventured out on their rounds. The mob and the riot were a nightmare of yesterday that had evanesced in the morning light.

But the cavalry troop riding at a discreet distance behind Seymour and Opdyke, sunlight glinting off saber blades, served as a reminder of what was still unloosed in the city.

. . . *3*

A BATTERING ram was needed to break down the iron door. Lane sent his men out to find one, and they located a thick crossbeam which had been left over from the construction of stables nearby and forgotten in the weeds of a back yard.

A dozen husky men lifted the beam and started pounding it rhythmically against the door. The metal portal clanged sonorously like a great gong. Paint chipped off from the blows and the pitted, rust corroded surface of the metal was exposed. The sweating men rushed forward again and again to crash the beam against the door.

A big crowd gathered to watch their efforts. Every time the beam struck the door, a wild cheer arose. Rioters pitched in to help. One hulking man had a sledge hammer which he swung in drunken anger, his thick muscles rippling under his torn shirt. A blow from the sledge dented the iron and the door began to buckle under the continuous pounding of the ram.

Sweat dripped from the men on the ram. Their hands were torn by the splintery surface of the beam. They drew back for another attempt and charged forward. The two leading men stumbled and fell to their knees, dropping the beam. The others, carried forward by the momentum, tumbled over their comrades and sprawled in the roadway. They breathed heavily; too exhausted to rise. Willing hands helped them to their feet, and others took up the battering ram as the weary men slumped on the ground trying to catch their breaths.

New enthusiasm filled the mob. The example set by these men sparked the rioters. Men and women staggered under the weight of paving blocks which they hurled at the door. Some beat against it with bare fists. A mass frenzy flashed through the crowd. The rioters struggled to get at the door; it shuddered under the onslaught. It had become a symbol to the mob of all the frustrating bitterness in their lives: the vile places in which they lived, the squalor and the meanness. The door was Lincoln and the War and the Draft. They flailed at it, cursing and shouting. All at once, the massive hinges were ripped free, and with an exultant cry they wrenched the door loose. The building was open—the crates of guns and the stores of ammunition were theirs.

They rushed into the place. Lane tried to bring some semblance of order but he and his men were shoved aside and scattered by the onpressing mob. Chaos took over. Lane was knocked from his feet and barely managed to escape being trampled. He was tossed to the edges of the swarming mass that fought to enter the building.

He saw John Andrews mounted on a horse, waving his arms and shouting, and tried to reach the man. But before he could get to him the frightened horse reared and threw Andrews heavily. The animal bolted and galloped away in maddened flight, reins and stirrups flying. At last Lane gained a path to Andrews. He pulled the dazed man out of the milling mass.

"Stand fast, you stupid bastards," Lane cried, trying to steady the people. "Get the guns out of the building!"

Nobody paid the slightest attention to him. Andrews stood beside him, his fine jacket torn, blood trickling from his nose and drying in his red beard. Lane shouted to him, "Do something. Speak to them. They'll listen to you!"

"They're out of their heads! I can't do anything!" Andrews said.

Fury gripped Lane. His eyes blazed maniacally. He grabbed Andrews by the lapels and drew him close. "Where are all your promises? Where are the men? How can we win with this lousy scum?" he shouted into Andrews' face.

"I don't know. I don't know. I'm in it, too. Oh, God, what's going to happen? What will become of us?" Andrews whimpered.

Lane pushed him away in disgust. He looked about contemptuously. The rioters were making carnival. Men leaned far out of the upper story windows waving and calling to friends in the street. Those below shouted back. Second Avenue swarmed with thousands capering, yelling and gesturing.

What was the good? Lane thought. No discipline. No control. He wanted men who knew how to obey. Men with pride; not these. His own lads were scattered somewhere in that roaring throng. Now that weapons were at hand, this rabble had to be organized and knit into fighting units. But they did not want that. It seemed to be enough for them to have broken down the door and captured the building. They had won a further excuse for drinking, and for untrammeled celebration.

Lane beat his fists against his thighs. He had lost command of the situation. All the weeks of careful planning, the carefully studied maps, the timetable accuracy of each move had been wasted and all because they had been forced to deal with double-crossing Yankee bastards. Men of that kind, men who played with treason, should never have been trusted. The Fernando Woods played the dangerous game. If the plan worked, they'd be on top. If it failed no one could prove anything against them.

Lane was a Virginian, a gentleman who deemed it an honor to die for Virginia and the Confederacy. But, if he had to die, let it be at the head of his own men and not in the company of this shabby mob. The feeling of personal doom overwhelmed him once again. He was desperately alone and that made him afraid. But at the moment when fear was about to control him, he saw Gordon moving toward him, the men following in a compact group. They had reassembled and re-formed ranks. The moment of fear was over for Ross. His men were there. No matter what might happen, he was going to be with them.

He turned to Andrews who tugged nervously at his beard. Lane spoke to him gently, "Cheer up, man. We'll figure a way. It isn't too late for us. . . ."

On Third Avenue, the leading lorry rolled to a stop at 21st Street and the policemen jumped out. The lorries halted one behind the other. Big Dan Carpenter bellowed at his men, urging them to fall in, quickly. The police obeyed and stood in perfect alignment. They could see and hear the mob on Second Avenue.

"Your orders are to clear the street, to make no arrests. Don't spare your clubs. Use firearms if necessary. And die like true Americans if you must!" Dan Carpenter shouted.

He pulled his cap more firmly on his head, pointed toward Second Avenue with his locust stick and cried, "Go get 'em, terriers!"

The policemen charged into Second Avenue. They slashed furiously with their sticks. Soon, the rioters were in flight. Many of them fled into houses and climbed to the roofs to shoot at the police. The officers rushed into the houses, kicked down doors and went up onto the rooftops. There, they tackled the snipers, hurling some into the street and killing others on the spot with macelike blows from the locust sticks.

The mob could not take the furious attack. Carpenter led his men slowly northward, past the Union Steam Works. He detached a force to drive the rioters from the building, which they did in short order. As the police advanced toward 33rd Street,

Captain Franklin and his regulars came up. They went in with fixed bayonets alongside the policemen. The avenue looked like a hard-fought battlefield.

Dead and dying rioters were strewn on the sidewalks and in the gutters from 21st to 33rd Streets. A band of them had fortified themselves in Riley's Porter House on the southeast corner of 32nd Street. From behind barricaded windows and the roof, they kept up a fire at the police and soldiers. A charge by a platoon of regulars forced an entry to the place through an unguarded door.

Once inside, the soldiers used musket butts and bayonets to drive the rioters into the street where they were caught and clubbed by Carpenter's men. The mob sullenly fled five or six blocks north and stood in uncertain ugliness. Carpenter had cowed them as effectively as he had the previous day on Broadway. But even so, the battle was not yet over.

Suddenly, a body of a hundred men armed with muskets detached itself from the mob and to the surprise of the watching police and soldiers marched in precise formation across the front of the throng. The men spread out into a firing line and opened up with sharp volleys that forced policemen and soldiers to scamper for cover.

Encouraged by this, the mob swept forward. Bricks and rocks pelted the outnumbered police and soldiers. They began to give ground, and the steady firing took its toll. A soldier fell, to be carried off by his comrades. A policeman was hit. Rioters crept back to the rooftops and opened fire from the rear.

Carpenter spotted the leader of the group of disciplined rioters and pointed him out to a squad of soldiers. "Get that man," he ordered. The soldiers emptied their muskets at him, but the man was unscathed although bullets chipped the cobblestones at his feet. He stood unflinchingly, directing his men with the coolness of a field commander. The rioters fought skillfully. They fired and moved. A volley kept the front busy while small detachments worked onto the flanks, taking cover behind doorways and fences.

The mob had found its courage. Men who were armed with revolvers or muskets dashed forward to join Lane. John Andrews stood on the firing line urging the mob to attack the police and soldiers. Lane knew the rioters who had taken the Union Steam Works had been driven from it. But he felt that a strong, concerted rush could recapture the building.

Grudgingly, he had to admit that the mob was standing up well. All they had needed was an example to follow and his men had given them that. He wondered how he could have felt this was his day of doom—it was going to be one of victory, instead.

Drawing his pistol, he called to his men and started on a run toward the Union Steam Works where police and soldiers were attempting to rally.

The rebel yell tore from his throat and the men behind him joined in with the high-pitched yipping battle cry that had echoed piercingly over so many desperately fought fields. And as the yell rose it brought a deep roar from the mob, a bellow of mass anger.

No one gave the rioters a signal or command. They simply pushed forward, cheering. A distance of four or five blocks separated them from the police and the regulars. The soldiers stood with bayonets bristling, prepared for the shock of the attack.

At that crucial moment, Colonel O'Brien appeared with the 11th New York Volunteers. The two artillery pieces had been delayed because a broken harness strap had held up one gun and Lieutenant Eagleson had remained with it, ordering the driver of the other caisson to stay with him while hasty repairs were made. Somewhere, young Eagleson had been taught that artillery must always be used in pairs to be most effective.

O'Brien was not a wise military man. His training had been

restricted to limited participation in a few battles in which he had distinguished himself for recklessness rather than strategy. But he did not have to be a von Clausewitz to size up this situation. He saw an avalanche of enraged humanity sweeping down on the tiny force that barred its way. Windows and rooftops were filled with hostile armed people. Unless quick action was taken, a catastrophe was in the making.

The Colonel drew his sword. "Into line!" he yelled at his troops. The soldiers swiftly formed a firing line, and moved into position beside Carpenter's and Franklin's men. The van of the mob was closing in only a block or so away.

"Fire! Damn it! Fire!" O'Brien shouted. A volley ripped from his front rank, then another from the second row. The regulars opened up and the mob stopped short. The great mob wavered and shuddered but did not break; only its forward movement was halted for the moment. Lane's men, their ranks depleted, sent a volley at the soldiers, but with the arrival of the 11th New York, there was too much fire power for them to slug it out in a stand-up fight. At Lane's signal they fell back. The mob, snarling in defiance, massed in the roadway. It was only a respite and Inspector Carpenter knew it. The sniper fire from the rooftops was galling. Several volleys from the troops cleared the snipers away, but one kept shooting at Carpenter, the bullets ricocheting around the Inspector. He spotted the man behind a chimney. The next time the sharpshooter came up, Carpenter took a shot at him with his revolver and the man tumbled to the street with a bullet in his head.

The clatter of horses and the grinding racket of iron wheels announced the arrival of the two field pieces. The caissons and limbers rocked and bounced over the cobblestones. Lieutenant Eagleson rode up to O'Brien and saluted the Colonel.

"Goddamn you, Eagleson! This isn't a parade ground! Stop saluting and get those pieces set up!" O'Brien cried.

Eagleson's cannoneers were ready in minutes as another ex-

change of musketry between soldiers and the mob growled into
life. A group of rioters made a sortie at the guns but were driven
back. That unsuccessful attack aroused the mob. A dark-haired
young woman jumped in front of the rioters. "If you're men, then
you'll go to glory!" she cried. "Are you free men or dogs?"

"Ah, shut up, Moll! Those bloody bluecoats would kill us all!"
a man bellowed angrily.

"No man lives forever," the girl cried. "Ain't it better to die at
home than fighting this dirty war? My John is dead. I'm asking
you to avenge him!"

They whispered to each other about her—Moll Shannon, whose
bridegroom had been killed at Chancellorsville only three months
after their marriage. Poor Moll, they said. She'd gone a bit daft
with grief. She was a pretty one with that raven black hair and
the pointed breasts and the red lips that hungered for a man.
The lass is right, they whispered, one to the other. Better to die
at home. Up and at them. The bloody peelers and the damned
soldiers. At them! The murdering bastards!

"We're with you, Moll!" they shouted.

Once more they went forward, pushing Lane and his men with
them, sweeping John Andrews up in the onrush. They shook
fists and waved clubs, and they were in full motion as O'Brien's
sword flashed in a glinting arc and he called on the cannoneers
to fire.

The guns belched orange flame and the grapeshot marked a
path of death. Moll Shannon fell, her lustrous black hair sopping
up the blood that formed a quick pool under her torn body.
Dozens fell. The mob turned into a jumbled and howling mass.
The guns went again and now the rioters sprinted in every direction. Still, some stood fast, driven to animal fury and senseless
bravery. Ross Lane and the handful of his men who had survived were among those. A man tore his shirt off and dipped it in
Moll Shannon's blood. He waved the crimson-hued garment over
his head.

"Revenge! Revenge for Moll!" he cried.

Men rallied to him as he charged on, waving the shirt like a flag. The onslaught reached the first line of regulars and the attackers were caught on the bayonet points. The man with the shirt was skewered by a sword thrust. The police went in with their sticks once more.

It was a wild, formless battle. Men rolled in the gutter grappling. A blow from a locust stick sent Lane reeling toward a low, spiked iron picket fence which ran across the front of a brownstone. He lost his balance and fell. He rose groggily and another policeman struck him. Lane pitched forward onto a spike and hung there, horribly impaled under the chin by the pointed picket.

The melee lasted only a bit longer. The rioters soon fled. Two policemen lifted Lane's body and placed him on the sidewalk. One of them studied the corpse as he knelt beside it. He opened the rough work shirt and cried out when he saw the expensive underwear. He called to Carpenter and showed him how the body was dressed.

"He's not one of them. By the saints, look at his hands. Those aren't the mitts of a worker," Carpenter said.

"Aye, sir," the policeman agreed. He searched Lane's pockets and found the watch, which he held up. "He's a gent, all right. Look at this ticker he's carrying."

Carpenter took the watch and snapped open the case. He examined the miniature in the back of the watch. He looked down at the dead man. Who was he, Carpenter wondered . . . this stranger in the mob? What was he doing there? Who were the people in the daguerreotype? Carpenter sighed. These were questions to which he would never know the answer. He glanced up the avenue. The bodies of those killed in the fighting dotted the street. A woman lay dead, an overturned shopping basket lying near her limp, outstretched hand. She had been an innocent housewife caught in the riot while shopping. Men lay piled across each other as the grapeshot had cut them down. Hate was forever frozen in their faces.

Carpenter turned away. He hated violence—but he was a policeman and these people had broken the law. If it took killing to restore peace, then that was how it had to be. Dan Carpenter was a simple, righteous man who had taken an oath as a police officer and meant to keep it.

This was to be their last fight and they knew it, each one of the few left from Lane's command. But no matter what happened now they were not going to leave the Captain's body with the Yankees. What a way for him to have died, hooked on that damn fence like a side of beef in a butcher's storeroom! It was hard to believe the Captain was dead. There was a soldier. He'd stand up there cool as a sip of spring water while the Minié balls zipped around him like bottle flies.

But what was the good of all that bravery now? He had died in the street without glory or dignity. By now, each of them knew he was being wasted on a wild mission. Perhaps the men had known it all along but none had voiced any complaints and nothing had been too much to perform.

Hell, they had done all men could do—and given all men could give. Now most of their comrades were dead and the living still had to give more. The Captain belonged to them and they were going to get him back.

Quickly and expertly, they loaded their muskets. They huddled briefly together and spoke in urgent whispers. Here was what had to be done, they decided! One group would pour a volley into the Yankees to keep them busy while the others rushed in and seized the Captain's body. Move now! Go now! No time for even the briefest handshakes or a whispered goodby to old friends. It was for the Captain they were doing this instead of high-tailing it out of there and saving their own skins.

They moved down the avenue, fanned wide to give as little

target as possible to the artillery. Those who had been selected opened fire. The volley drove the Yankees under cover. The confusion did not last long but it was time enough for several men to dash in and toss Lane's body onto a makeshift litter and carry it away.

Later, Lane's body, weighted with heavy stones, was heaved into the East River. As the ripples widened, they saluted their captain for the last time, then separated and the maze of the city swallowed them.

John Andrews had been running for what seemed to him an eternity. His lungs ached and a searing stitch slashed through his chest. But he did not stop. He ran on, past blurred faces and voices which called to him. He pushed through the mob and some tried to stop his flight, but Andrews tore loose from the clutching hands. He ran through a weird and stinking hell of smoke and death. And always before him he saw Ross Lane hanging from the fence with the cruel spike buried under his chin and his glazed, dead eyes staring sightlessly. . . .

Andrews ran for a long time, up one block and down another, until he reached a house on a peaceful street that was untouched by riot and violence. Close by stood the stately, elegant mansions of Fifth Avenue. The mob seemed part of another world, here, on East 11th Street. Andrews leaned against the wrought-iron gate and stared at the house. The shutters were closed against the hot sun and inside, Andrews knew, would be a cool, shadowed sanctuary. The great oak tree on the wide lawn cast deep shade across the stoop. At first he could only stand there, drawing breath in sobbing gasps like a frightened animal that had escaped the hunting pack and miraculously reached the safety of a secret den.

Even after a few minutes, his hands still trembled although he had regained some composure. He had seen all he wanted of mobs and violence and destruction. No one would find him here and when all this quieted down he could leave the city—maybe go out West. In spite of the war, a smart operator could do well out there with a saloon or a gambling hall.

After all, what the hell did he care if a bunch of clodhoppers were drafted? He'd been paid for what he'd done—to make speeches and stir up the rabble. They'd had big plans, the Copperheads. Capture the arsenals and the telegraph stations, the banks and the railroads. They'd merely been waiting for the right moment, the politicians had said. Well, the moment had come—and now it was gone. The dumb immigrants who believed all the talk were getting themselves slaughtered and God alone knew how many were dead.

The riot had been great fun for a while, riding the white horse with everybody cheering him. That was finished now. John Andrews wasn't one to stand up before cannon and muskets and locust clubs. War wasn't for him. He had found that out a long time ago when he'd deserted in Mexico with the officers' mess fund of the old 4th Infantry. What a time he'd had with that loot. What a memory!

He smiled to himself as he opened the gate and walked up the short path to the front door. He yanked the bell handle and heard it ring inside the quiet house. This was a peaceful world filled with the scent of blooming roses and the twittering of sparrows perched in the oak tree.

Once beyond the door with the gleaming brass knob, in the serenity of the rosewood and tapestry parlor, all the horror he had seen and experienced would fade away—even the memory of Ross Lane, ghastly in death.

The door opened and a tall brown-skinned woman stood there. She looked at him nervously and said, "John, what's happened? You're a sight."

"Nothing a hot bath and some fresh clothes won't fix, Josephine," he said.

He stepped across the threshold and she closed the door. "I'm in trouble," he said.

"You only come to me when there's trouble," she said flatly.

He patted her cheek lightly.

"I'll draw your bath. Come upstairs," she said. Her voice was soft, tinged with the touch of the bayou and swamp, and the smokiness of nighttime cabin fires was in her skin. He followed her contentedly, his feet sinking into the soft nap of the stair carpeting.

Josephine West was mistress of the most exclusive whorehouse in New York. Many of the city's prominent men were her customers, and her quadroon girls, asleep in their rooms on the top floor, were both expensive and beautiful. She had been Andrews' mistress for some years now, a secret both kept well.

She led him to a luxurious bedroom on the second floor. "I'll heat water for you, John," she said.

Downstairs, she entered the parlor, went to a mahogany desk, found paper and pen and wrote a brief note:

> Sergeant Young:
> He is here. Come quickly.
> Josephine West

She folded the paper carefully and put it in an envelope. She went into the kitchen where a young white man was seated by the round table, drinking coffee. He was a tough Five Points youth whom she had befriended. He worked for her as messenger, carriage driver and handy man. She handed him the envelope and said, "Jimmy, take this to Sergeant Young."

Jimmy smiled crookedly. "I know where to find him, Josie. I'll deliver it."

He slipped out the back door. Josephine sat down in a kitchen chair. For a little while she stared at the wall, stony-faced. Then she wept softly. When she had learned from the morning papers that John Andrews was a leader of the mob, she had contacted Sergeant Young, knowing that Andrews would come to her eventually. And because she was a Negro woman and knew the fear and the degradation of her people, she was prepared to betray the man she loved.

. . . *4*

SERGEANT John Young looked glumly from the window of his office. Below, the street was bustling. As units were given marching orders, the drummer boys beat the long roll. In the courtyard, citizen volunteers were being issued locust clubs and revolvers. An ammunition convoy was unloaded by soldier details. Hundreds of Negroes roamed the street, weeping, praying, standing in dazed silence. A long line shuffled slowly toward an army field kitchen where hot food was being dispensed by sweating cooks.

Young was standing with his back to the three men who sat wearily on cane chairs in his office. At last, he turned and spoke to them. "Boys, there's no use mourning about it. Andrews got away and that's that."

Detective Tom Dusenberry who had been sullenly regarding his scuffed work shoes looked up and said, "You should have let me finish him off when we had the chance."

Young smiled. "You know better, Tom. You and Farley and Eustace did your best——"

"We're lucky to have come out alive," Eustace said.

"It was rough, Sergeant," Phil Farley said. "People were killed

all around us. You never saw such confusion as when those cannon opened up. Andrews simply disappeared. For all we know,
he's dead, too."

"No such luck. Bastards like that don't die," Dusenberry said.

Young flexed his fingers. "I've had no word from Josephine
West," he said.

"I've known Josie ten years. I'd never have thought she would
get tied up with a son of a bitch like Andrews," Dusenberry
said.

"She promised me to send word if he showed," Young said.

"How do you know she'll keep her word?" Eustace asked.

"She's never broken it to me," Young said.

"I get around a lot and I've never even heard a whisper about
them," Dusenberry said.

"Josie knows how to keep her trap shut," Farley said.

"I can't see why she ever promised to sing. It isn't like her,"
Eustace said.

"I'll tell you why. She told me Andrews had done the colored
people a great wrong. She loves him but even love isn't enough
to forgive what he's done. When she sent for me, I thought it
might be a wild goose chase. But we sat there in her parlor
and she told me how she felt about Andrews, but since learning he was with the mob she wanted to do something for her
people. Figured the most she could do would be to turn him
in. That's all there is to it, lads," Young said.

He could understand what it must have meant to the woman
to discover that her lover was a murderer of her own people.
He felt sorry for her.

The detectives fell silent. They could only hope that Andrews
would be delivered to them by his mistress.

The fighting was ended on Second Avenue and the Union
Steam Works with its valuable guns was safe. Carpenter marched
his men back to headquarters after a tour of the area. A large

police detachment of one hundred men stayed to guard the building under command of Captain John Helme, 27th Precinct, who had been ordered to remove all the weapons stored at the Union Steam Works and load them onto vans that had been commandeered to take them down to Mulberry Street. The job was completed successfully. Escorted by the police, the vans moved off in convoy through the deserted streets.

After a while, men and women who had participated in the riot returned to look for friends and relatives among the dead and wounded. Morgue wagons took the bodies to the mortuary. Ambulances picked up the wounded. A local doctor reported treating twenty-one head injuries, all of them proving fatal.

Neighborhood people congregated on street corners and talked over the events of the past forty-eight hours. They gathered in curious groups around the Union Steam Works and examined the picket fence on which Lane had died. They came to the spot where Moll Shannon had fallen, looking morbidly at the great splash of blood that darkened the cobblestones. In many of the tenement houses along Second Avenue, women mourned their dead. Men with bloodied bandages around their heads lay moaning, and wide-eyed children stood in the doorways of bedrooms staring at pain-wracked men—fathers, sons, husbands— all victims of the morning's carnage.

Second Avenue was littered with mementos of the riot—pieces of bloodstained clothing; a broken musket; rocks, bottles, bricks that had been thrown; a bayonet scabbard; a door frame splintered by grapeshot; gaping windows where the glass had been knocked out. And each of these were embers to keep hatred burning.

A great portion of the anger was turned against Colonel O'Brien. To the rioters, he was a murderer because it was he who had ordered the artillery to fire upon his neighbors.

With the same illogic that had led them to believe they had

license to begin the riot, these people were convinced that any punishment meted against them was unjust. The policemen they called "bloody butchers" and the soldiers were "Lincoln's cutthroats." But the brutalities they had inflicted were not to be impugned.

A large crowd drifted toward O'Brien's house on 34th Street near Second Avenue. Irate people threw rocks at the windows, but the shutters were drawn and very little damage resulted. The Colonel's wife, a cautious woman, had taken her two small children to Brooklyn early in the morning, feeling that they would be safer in Flatlands with her sister away from the riotous city. She had been unable to contact him as he had been on duty at the Armory all night.

The people milled about and muttered threats to burn the house down, but dispersed quickly and without resistance when a troop of cavalry rode through the area. A lassitude settled over the neighborhood. The anger was still evident but it had become an undercurrent.

Then, just before noon, Colonel O'Brien appeared, riding up Second Avenue. He had reported back to General Brown with the 11th Regiment. Brown cavalierly dismissed O'Brien, ordering him back to the Armory. The General's attitude irked the Colonel and an angry exchange of words followed. This outburst ended abruptly when Brown warned O'Brien to leave promptly or find himself escorted by the provost guard. O'Brien left, still muttering darkly.

Before making his way to the Armory, he decided to check on the safety of his wife and children. If he had been a more prudent man, he would have seen the folly of going into a hostile neighborhood such a short time after a battle.

He was neither prudent nor reasonable and so continued back to Second Avenue. Still fuming over General Brown's treatment of him, O'Brien stopped off at several saloons and downed several straight whisky shots.

He rode his horse into Second Avenue at 19th Street and proceeded slowly up the avenue, eying the people on the sidewalks with arrogant disdain. He stopped at his residence for news of his wife; learning that she was safe in Brooklyn, he remounted his horse and started downtown once more.

Word spread through the vicinity that O'Brien was there. Hostile crowds filled the sidewalks. As O'Brien rode away, men ran alongside hooting and threatening him.

"Nigger-loving traitor! Shooting down your own!" a man shouted.

The man jumped into the roadway and grabbed the horse's bridle. O'Brien turned beet red with anger. He pulled his heavy cavalry pistol from its holster and leveled it at the man.

"Drop that bridle, you gutter bastard, or I'll blow you to hell!" he shouted.

The erstwhile attacker dropped the straps and moved off. O'Brien stood up in the stirrups and swung the long barreled weapon in a slow, steady arc.

"Stand clear of me, you lousy scum," he said.

The crowd, which had gathered in the roadway, blocking his path, fell away. The people knew his black temper and that he would shoot without much more provocation. As they made a path for him, O'Brien sneered. He settled back in the saddle, holstered his revolver and went on at a steady gait, his beefy body jouncing up and down.

Faces scowled at him from windows. Sullen men shook fists behind his back. Yet, no one could gather the courage to fire a shot at him or throw a stone. Not satisfied with having cowed the mob, O'Brien foolishly decided to show his complete contempt.

There was a drug store at the corner of 18th Street and Second Avenue where whisky was dispensed. He reined in his horse, dismounted and slowly tied the animal to a hitching post. With a stiff, military bearing, he strode into the drug store and bought a drink which he sipped with insolent deliberation, staring out at the crowd that was gathering in front of the shop.

He emptied the glass and stepped into the street. Now, a surly mob blocked him. O'Brien drew his sword and his revolver. With a backhanded slash he hit the man nearest him across the face, using the flat of the sword. A way was parted for him and he walked toward his horse. He had not taken more than two or three steps when someone slugged him from behind with an empty whisky bottle. The blow sent him to his hands and knees and the mob swarmed on him. Men jumped on his thick chest. They kicked and beat him. Women rushed to tear his hair and his beard, yanking out fistfuls by the roots.

The rioters dragged him by the legs to the cobblestoned gutter. Children joined the torture and jabbed him with sharpened sticks. They hauled him up Second Avenue. They tore the clothes from him. Screeching women slashed his flesh with paring knives. They tugged him naked and bleeding into his own back yard and inflicted gruesome atrocities on him, which an eyewitness described as "more grisly than the worst actions of the most barbarous red-skinned savages."

Miraculously, O'Brien stayed alive through all this ordeal. He was close to death and bloody froth formed on his lips but a spark of life refused to be extinguished. Because he still lived, the mob became even more infuriated and worse outrages than before were committed against him.

A man found a huge rock in the yard which he dropped onto O'Brien's chest, but even this could not kill him. He kept groaning and rattling in his throat. At last someone in that crowd took pity on him. O'Brien was a devout Catholic, and the rioter went to a nearby church where he informed the parish priest, Father Edward Cowery, what was happening. The elderly priest hurried to the scene and tried to reach the dying man's side. The rioters blocked him and tried to hold him back. In the ensuing scuffle, someone struck the priest in the mouth. Blood trickled from his torn lip and he cried out in a terrible voice, "What manner of people are you to stand in the way of God's servant?"

The sight of the blood on the priest brought a shamed silence. The torturers slunk back and Father Cowery went to the unsightly body and knelt by it. He saw that O'Brien had only minutes left to live and began praying. Some of O'Brien's murderers crossed themselves as they heard the words of the priest.

"Proficiscere anima Christiana, de hoc mundo, in nomine de patris omnipotentis qui te creavit, in nomine Jesu Christi filii dei vivi . . ." the priest chanted, and O'Brien died.

. . . 5

A RUMOR spread that the Brooklyn Navy Yard was under danger of imminent attack by a well-armed and well-led mob. At the first whisper of this, Rear Admiral Hiram Paulding ordered all approaches to the Navy Yard covered.

The receiving ship, *North Carolina*, 40 guns; the corvette *Savannah*, 22 guns; the steam gunboats *Granite City*, *Gertrude*, and *Unadilla*, 8 guns apiece, and the *Tulip*, 6 guns, steamed into position, cannon shotted and decks stripped for action.

At the same time, the ironclad battery *Passaic* and the steamboat *Fuchsia* moved to action stations off the Battery to intercept any move toward Governor's Island.

General Wool sent a message to Captain Stephen Sluyter of the *Tulip* which instructed him on the action to take if the mob attempted to loot the subtreasury:

HEADQUARTERS, DEPARTMENT OF THE EAST
New York, July 14, 1863

Captain Sluyter, commanding gunboat *Tulip* off foot of Wall Street:
Sir:

In accordance with arrangement between you and Mr. J. J. Cisco, assistant treasurer, United States Sub-Treasury, you are hereby authorized to open fire on Wall or Pine Street or both, if signalled accordingly.

John E. Wool
Major General

Hourly, the embattled city drew its lines tighter. By noon on Tuesday, all the forces which could be mustered were under arms. Naval gun crews manned loaded cannon and guarded the important Government buildings, the Customs House, the Sub-Treasury and the Federal Court House.

A cavalry encampment, complete with tents, sentries and bugle calls, was set up in Madison Square Park under the command of the glamorous Gettysburg hero, Brigadier General Judson Kilpatrick. Across the street from the bivouac stood the Fifth Avenue Hotel. The stylish lobby was thronged with spurred and booted young cavalry officers who twirled their mustaches and strutted about with much saber rattling under the admiring eyes of pretty girls.

A letter arrived at Police Headquarters addressed to Commissioner Acton which said:

Commissioner and Conspirator against your State and the People: Prepare to meet your God!

(Signed)

By Advice of the Committee.

But despite the riot and the tensions, the clocks in church steeples and on public buildings sounded the hour of noon with comforting mellow chimes—a serene note in the tumultuous city.

In the Mayor's office the City Hall clock's sonorous tones were muffled. Governor Seymour stood by the Mayor's desk, gnaw-

ing at his lower lip with poorly concealed impatience and nerv-
ousness. Opdyke paced back and forth and neither man spoke.
When the great clock's tolling stopped there was an uneasy
silence between the men. Outside the noises of a large but orderly crowd could be heard. For more than an hour, thousands
had streamed into Printing House Square to hear Seymour. The
people came in response to the placards that advertised his
scheduled address from the side steps of City Hall.

Elaborate precautions were taken for the protection of the
Hall and the important officials. Cannon covered the Park and
the area where the crowd had assembled. Sharpshooters stood
on the roofs of nearby buildings. Files of soldiers with bayoneted muskets were drawn up in battle order.

At last the moment had arrived. Seymour was well aware
that this was going to be one of the most important speeches
of his career. He reviewed the points he intended to make. For
an instant, he permitted his thoughts to wander to the peaceful hours he had spent in the country with the sun and the sea-
freshened breezes in his face. But those hours were gone—and
he was here in the hot city with the noonday sun beating down
on the great assemblage he was to address. If anything, the
temperature had risen since the heat of the morning.

Seymour cleared his throat and said, "Mayor Opdyke, will you
come out and stand with me?"

"I don't think so. That crowd has come to hear you. My presence won't lend weight to your appeal," Opdyke said. "It is better for you to go alone. Otherwise the crowd might suspect that
this is some kind of a Republican trick."

He smiled at Seymour and extended his hand. "Good luck,
sir." The men shook hands warmly. The Governor drew a deep
breath, pulled himself erect and stepped out into the hallway.
There, the Deputy Sheriff of New York County, Theodore Dunlap, was awaiting him. Dunlap led him to a side entrance and

opened the door. The two men stepped out into the glare of sunlight.

The brightness made Seymour blink. Before him, all of Printing House Square seemed filled with masses of onlookers. Beyond them he saw *The Tribune* building with the muzzles of Gatling guns jutting down from the windows of an upper floor. He saw the array of soldiers interposed between him and the crowd, officers with drawn swords and soldiers impassive and stolid, the sunlight tipping their bayonets. As the crowd became aware of his presence a rolling cry came from it.

"Seymour! Seymour!" they shouted.

The swelling roar echoed across the Square and faded in the Park. Sheriff Dunlap stepped forward and said, "Citizens of New York City, I give you His Excellency, Horatio Seymour, Governor of our glorious Empire State!"

Another shout arose and as it died out, Seymour walked to the edge of the steps and stretched his arms out to the throng. "My friends," he said, "I have come down here from the quiet of the country to see what the difficulty was, to learn what all the trouble was concerning the draft. Let me assure you that I am your friend."

"We know it, Horatio! We know it!" his listeners cried.

"You have been my friends——" he began, but shouts from the audience drowned him out.

"Yes, yes, that's so! We are and we will be again!" they yelled.

"And I assure you, my fellow citizens, that I am here to show you a test of my friendship. I wish to inform you that I have sent my adjutant general to Washington to confer with the authorities there, to have this draft suspended and stopped. I now ask you as good citizens to wait for his return, and I assure you that I will do all that I can to see that there is no inequality and no wrong done to anyone. I want you to take good care of all property and see that every person is safe. It is your duty to maintain the good order of the city and I know you will do it. When my adjutant returns from Washington you shall be satisfied. Listen to me and see that no harm is done either to persons or property, but retire peaceably. I ask you to leave me now in the confidence that I will see to your rights."

The speech was finished. A splattering of applause sounded feebly in the crowd.

Men shouted, "Send away the soldiers! Send away the blue-coated bastards!"

Seymour stood still. He felt an emptiness, a sense of futility: he had not proven adequate to the situation. This crowd neither believed him nor would it do what he had asked.

The crowd's sullen muttering took on a threatening tone. The soldiers moved in with lowered bayonets and a cavalry troop, sabers drawn, rode into the mass and started to edge the people out of the Square. The crowd shuffled and eddied about, stubbornly refusing to leave. Boos and catcalls came to the Governor. He turned and walked heavily into City Hall through the side door.

Where had he failed, he asked himself. He had spoken to the people honestly and simply—as a friend—but it had not been enough. He had simply told them the truth, but they did not care about truth. They demanded more from him—something he could not give. He had done all in his power to fight the draft, but that was not enough.

And he had made an even more serious error. Even as he was speaking, mobs were rampaging through the city. His words had been wasted. Those gathered to hear him were not rioters. They were frightened people looking to him for a panacea, an announcement that the draft had been repealed and they were safe from it. These people were on the border line—teetering between peaceful, law-abiding behavior and the tumultuous excesses of rioting.

He was depressed by the dubious outcome of his effort to mollify them. No gain would result from his speech. He had

had enough experience with crowds to recognize their temper
and he was unhappily aware that he had lost this one.

Even in the recessed shadows of the corridor he heard angry
shouting as people grudgingly retreated under pressure of soldiers and horsemen, only to gather again some blocks away.
This time, not as a docile crowd—but as a dangerous and raging mob.

Freshly shaved and bathed, his beard and hair pomaded so
the red locks gleamed coppery in the sunlight, John Andrews
stood on the little balcony that led from the bedroom and over-
looked the pleasant garden with its splashing fountain and flowers laid out in multicolored tiers. He leaned on the curved
wrought-iron railing, puffing on a cigar. Lazy summer sounds—
droning bees, tinkling water, twittering birds—made a peaceful
background to the sunshine and the cloudless sky.

He thought only briefly of the morning and its appalling
events. Somewhere, a steeple clock chimed noon. At that moment, a mile or so to the south, Governor Seymour was ready to
address the gathering in Printing House Square. About a mile
to the north, sadistic rioters were torturing Colonel O'Brien.
But there was no sign of such ferment in this place. Andrews
flicked the ash from his cigar and stroked his beard.

He stepped into the room and eyed himself in the full-length
oval mirror by the massive wardrobe chest. His white linen suit
was spotless and flawlessly pressed. His shirt was made of the
best French lisle, his gleaming shoes of the softest English
leather. Josie was a good wench. She gave him the best and
paid for it, too.

His reflection pleased him. He smiled and saluted his image
with a carefree wave of his hand. Suddenly, the bedroom door
was thrown violently open and three men attired in ordinary
work clothes burst in. He went icy with fear and could only
stare at them in amazement.

"Who are you? What do you want?" he managed to say.

One of them, a husky man with bristling mustaches, stepped up to him. He put his hand on Andrews' arm and said, "We're police officers. I'm Detective Tom Dusenberry and these men are Detectives Farley and Eustace. In the name of New York City, I arrest you, John Andrews!"

Andrews turned ashen. He pulled away from Dusenberry. "You're not police! This is some trick!" he cried.

Tom Dusenberry scowled. "Look, my bucko, we're not here for games. You know we're the police. And there's a carriage waiting downstairs. Are you coming peaceably or do you choose to leave feet first?"

"Why are you arresting me? I've done nothing! I know my rights! I'm a lawyer! I demand to hear the charges against me!" Andrews cried.

Dusenberry cocked a huge fist. "Charges? Why you black-hearted bastard——"

Farley grabbed him by the arm. "Easy, Tom."

Still seething, Dusenberry managed to control his temper. "All right, Phil, all right. I'll not lay a finger on him," he said. "So you want to know the charges, do you? Then listen. Inciting to riot, arson, murder, treason," he recited, ticking the counts off on his fingers.

"I don't understand. Treason, murder, arson, riot. Gentlemen, gentlemen, I assure you that some ghastly mistake has been made," Andrews said with a sickly smile.

Detective Eustace who had been standing quietly, leaning against the door jamb with his arms folded, straightened up and pointed a forefinger at Andrews. "Now, surely you aren't denying you took part in the rioting this morning and yesterday? Or that you spoke to the mob that burned the Provost Marshal's office on Third Avenue?" he asked.

"I do deny it! I do!" Andrews cried. Sweat formed on his forehead. He fingered his beard and licked his lips. "I deny it! I was here in this house! All the time—yesterday—today! I'll prove it to you! I'll prove it!" He grew incoherent and gibbering, pushed past the detectives into the hallway where he cried hoarsely, "Josie! Josie! Come here! I need you!"

His voice echoed frantically in the hall and sounded throughout the big house. On the top floor, the girls stirred awake as his hysterical outcries pierced their heavy slumber.

Again he cried and again, "Josie! Oh, my God! Josie! Josie!" The detectives began to lead him down the stairway but he clung desperately to each post of the banister and they had to pry his fingers loose at every step. He clutched the newel post at the foot of the stairs with desperate strength. The detectives struggled with him as he flung himself wildly about, thrashing and screaming. He broke from them, his arms flailing. Dusenberry stepped in and punched him in the kidneys. Andrews doubled over, wheezing in pain. The officers hustled him onto the stoop.

Josephine was standing there. Her girls, fully awake, poked their heads out of the upstairs windows, faces puffy and squint-eyed in the unaccustomed sunlight. She stood in front of Andrews and he moaned, "Tell them it's a mistake, Josie. I was here with you. Tell them."

She looked at him without emotion. Her face was like a beautiful mahogany mask. "It's no mistake. You were out in the streets with those others. You made your speeches and yelled for nigger blood. For my blood. What do you think I am? You think I forget my people because I run a fancy whorehouse and sleep with a white man? You could've done anything you wanted to, to me. But not this—not murder my people! I turned you in, John. I sent for the police. I want you to remember that."

He stared at her in dismay. "You? You did that? Oh, my God, Josie! They'll hang me!" he wailed. "They'll hang me for what I've done!"

"I hope they do," she said, and turned away and entered the house. Inside, she leaned against the door and closed her eyes.

Tears were hot under her lids and rolled down her smooth cheeks leaving shiny trails on the gloss of her dark skin. She remained like that until she heard the wheels of the carriage and the clopping of a horse and as she listened the sound died away. Only the chirping birds in the oak challenged the silence. . . .

They brought him to Police Headquarters and when word spread of the prisoner's identity angry policemen went into the detention room to get him. Only swift intervention by Commissioner Acton stopped them from beating him. When the troops heard Andrews was in the building they demanded that Acton turn him over to them.

Men from the Invalid Corps, who had escaped from the mob on Third Avenue the day before, struggled with Andrews' guards in an attempt to reach him. Old General Brown and the other officers managed to bring order by using the flats of their swords on the men.

During these disturbances, Andrews sat on a chair in Acton's office, wearing handcuffs and leg irons. He rocked back and forth and gibbered idiotically. Young questioned him at length but was not able to get any sense from the prisoner. At last the authorities decided it would be wiser to transfer him from Police Headquarters. A detail of marines took him to Fort Lafayette. He was locked in a basement cell where he raved and howled and beat his head against the slimy walls. The officer of the guard ordered him placed in a strait jacket and chained to his cot.

The telegraph wires at Police Headquarters were swamped with appeals for help. An urgent call came from the upper reaches of the city. A mob had set fire to houses on 129th Street and Third Avenue. Men had broken into the Red Bird Livery Stable on Sixth Avenue and were stealing horses to form a cavalry troop. Fire ravaged Allerton's Hotel on Eleventh Avenue and 41st Street. Buildings occupied by Negroes on Roosevelt Street were burned.

The pace of the rioting stepped up. At one point during midafternoon Acton had dispatched all his policemen, while Brown had ordered every available soldier out to break up mobs. Headquarters was manned only by Acton, Brown, Hawley, the telegraphers and the Negro refugees. An assault by a mob could easily have taken the building. But these were the calculated risks that had to be taken. General Brown kept two loaded revolvers on the table before him and seemed almost eager for the mob to put in an appearance.

Troubles piled up on the city's defenders. Roaming groups of rioters went about the city cutting telegraph wires. No sooner did a line go dead than Crowley sent out heavily armed repair crews to locate and mend the damage. The repairmen were worn out and tried to snatch a little sleep between calls.

A little while after Governor Seymour's speech, a band of rioters about three hundred strong marched on *The Tribune*, determined to hang Greeley and to burn the building down. One look at the cannon and Gatling guns and the sandbagged breastworks with soldiers behind them sent that mob scurrying off.

Clashes flared and died. Troops and police fought the rioters wherever mobs formed. Snipers exchanged shots across rooftops. The sound of gunfire was constant all over the city. It skipped elusively from one place to another. Sometimes it came in single, vicious shots. Sometimes, in deafening volleys that rattled the windows for blocks.

COMMISSIONER Acton sipped coffee from a thick white mug. The brew was hot and it burned in his throat as he drank. He needed that coffee, for sleep was gnawing at him, dragging down his arms and legs. His eyes were burning and pain beat in his temples. He had never known such fatigue—yet he felt a sense of exhilaration.

He managed to shut out, for the moment, the clicking telegraph senders, the many voices, the tramping of soldiers and the grating wagon wheels in the busy street.

For a minute he thought longingly of his study in his home on West 15th Street near Fifth Avenue. It was a proper brownstone for a respectable gentleman. Thomas Acton was certainly respectable—eminently so. He dealt in orderly matters—stocks and bonds and commodity shares. He was a successful broker and the unostentatious luxury of his home—the mahogany and rosewood furniture, the sterling tableware, the fragile bone china dishes, the damask tablecloths—reflected his success.

His daughters had married well. His wife was a gentlewoman, an excellent mother and a gifted hostess. She played the piano well and sang to her own accompaniment after dinner when the guests sat in the comfortable parlor. Would he ever again hear her in his own home in peace and tranquillity?

The city was strife-torn. Men were getting killed and he was ordering them to their deaths. Tom Acton, broker, gambled with inanimate stocks and bonds on the market. Tom Acton, Police Commissioner, gambled with lives. He felt himself falling into a doze, and forced his eyes open. He was seated at the long table. Maps of the city were spread out on it and the table top was littered with crumpled telegrams, empty coffee cups, notes and pencils.

Nearby, General Brown bent over a map and spoke earnestly with an artillery officer, a fat unkempt major from a western regiment who chewed tobacco and spurted juice on the floor.

Acton envied the General. Although Brown was almost seventy years old and had been on duty all night, the leathery veteran showed no signs of weariness. He seemed to thrive on this work—and in all the bustle of the big smoke-filled room, only the General seemed fresh and unruffled. He was shaved and his uniform was properly buttoned, even to the tight dog collar of the blouse. He wore his sword, and the piercing eyes in his craggy face were sharply alert. This was a man doing the job for which he had been preparing himself these many years. If Acton dealt in stocks and bonds, Brown was a merchant in artillery shells, bullets and death.

Acton had now become a partner in that very business. A reluctant partner, for when he had been appointed President of the Police Board, he had accepted the honor as a mark of civic recognition. It was a job for an executive, not a policeman; in his wildest imaginings he had never expected to find himself in a predicament such as this.

He was a man accustomed to the solidity of the Union League Club, the polite and gentlemanly behavior of the drawing room, and the hustling commercial atmosphere of the Stock Exchange and the countinghouses. Suddenly, he found himself surrounded by the crudeness of a military encampment—the sharp commands of noncoms, the clatter of muskets, the jangling of sabers and spurs. He was in the midst of the sights and sounds of a battlefield—bloodied faces, groaning wounded, and the biting smell of gunpowder.

To his astonishment, he found it suited him. He was swept with a sense of excitement that overcame both his weariness and his repugnance for violence. He felt a unity with the policemen who marched away to face either death or injury without hesitation. And he felt close to the soldiers, the strange,

calm young men who looked like boys playing a game of mas-
querade in their blue uniforms. Outside, a company was lounging at its ease. The smoke of the coffee fires drifted in through
the open windows. The insouciant ring of youthful voices came
to him. He heard them singing:

> "Let the wide world, wag as it will,
> We'll be gay and happy still. . . ."

This was a time for youth and courage. Yet the young men
brought to him the full horror of the war.

General Brown finished his conversation with the major who
saluted and went off to his assigned task with the casualness
of a shopkeeper opening his store for the day's business. He
spat a last stream of tobacco juice and waddled upstairs.

Brown stepped over to Acton. "Commissioner, there's real
work for us," the General said. He motioned for Acton to follow
him. The Commissioner rose and stretched his cramped limbs.
Brown led him to a map and pointed to a section of the city.
"This is a trouble spot," Brown said. The area he indicated was
in the neighborhood of Ninth Avenue between 40th and 45th
Streets.

"The rebels have put up barricades here," the General said.
"And they're well manned with riflemen. We've got to get them
out of there. I've ordered Major Watkins to move three artillery
batteries into position. Captain Wesson is available with a force
of my regulars. Can you let me have some police?"

Acton pursed his lips. "I think so. Captain George Walling
has a good sized detachment at the 20th Precinct, and Captain
Slott can use the reserve of the 22nd. I'd say that would give
you almost three hundred men."

"Excellent. When can they be ready to move?"

Acton glanced at the watch he took from his pocket. "It's
three, now. I'd say by five. How is that, sir?"

"Should be time enough. Will you give the orders, Commissioner? I believe the rendezvous should be at one of the police stations."

"How about the 20th Precinct?"

"Let's see, that's on 35th Street near Ninth Avenue, isn't it?"

"Right, General."

"Suits me. I'll order Wesson to march there."

The General nodded to Acton and signaled to his aides. The officers joined him and they hurried up the stairs. Acton dictated the necessary orders to a telegrapher. Walling and Slott were good officers and well equipped for the job he had assigned to them. Outside, the long roll was beating and the sound of the drums matched the racing hearts of the men who responded to it.

The barricades along Ninth Avenue, like those in Mackerelville, were made of carts lashed together with rope. Barrels, old furniture, anything else handy was also used. The rioters had pushed abandoned cars of the Ninth Avenue Street Railroad across the roadway to block it. Telegraph poles were cut down and laid crosswise to close off the side streets. House tops were turned into strong vantage points. Boys made piles of bricks from chimneys and collected ash cans which were placed at the edges of the roofs in position to be rolled down on any police or military who might put in an appearance.

The mob held riotous control of the neighborhood. Armed men patrolled the avenue between 40th and 45th Streets in boisterous groups. Others sat behind the barricades and waited. The day was hot and the mob had congregated many hours earlier. Some of the rioters had been out since 5:00 A.M. and the fun was beginning to wear a bit thin. The liquor stores and saloons had been cleaned dry. There was little left to drink in that area. The sun grew unbearable as the temperature climbed into the nineties. The tarred roofs of the houses melted in the heat, and the sidewalk pavement burned through even thick-soled work shoes.

Manning the barricades had become an irksome business without even a drop of whisky to wash the dust from a man's throat. Those rioters who were posted on the barricades grumbled about their lot—hell, who wanted to be cooked alive in the afternoon sun? A rumor started that three men had dropped from sunstroke on 45th Street.

Roving bands of rioters came through with gleeful reports of high doings in other places. They told about ransacking mansions and wine cellars and breaking into liquor stores. The drunkenness of the visitors was proof they were telling the truth. The riot seemed to be a grand ball for everyone except the restive men behind the barricades.

A burly rough known as "The Duster" leaned on his musket, spat disgustedly and said, "Hell, we ought to be shagging niggers instead of hanging around here and frying our brains out. What the hell good are we doing anyway? Ain't nobody coming to chase us out."

"Right, Duster, right," said a man who was sitting in a small patch of shadow cast by a shoulder high barricade.

"What we need is a drink," another chimed in.

"And where will you be getting it? There ain't a grogshop with anything left for blocks," The Duster growled.

A woman on the curbstone nearby cried out, "If you wasn't a bunch of thickheaded jackasses you'd know well enough where there's all the liquor you'll be wanting for the taking."

"And where might that be, Bridget?" The Duster asked, scowling at the skinny woman who smiled and simpered at a group of her cronies who clustered around.

"Why you blackhearted ape, at Johnny Flanagan's saloon, the dirty nigger-loving Republican," she said.

"That's right, Duster. That's right. Flanagan's saloon at the Weehawken Ferryhouse. She's right. And he deserves it, too. The Republican bastard! Let's show him, Duster, hey?" a man exclaimed.

The Duster frowned thoughtfully, angry with himself because he had not come up with the idea. "If you lads want to, I'll not say you no. I have no love for Flanagan," he said.

The men crowded around in an excited knot. One skinny, dried-up rioter waved his thin arms and said, "Flanagan took the bread out of me mouth, he did. I worked for him and he gave me the sack. Hired a Republican nigger-lover, he did. Took the bread out of me mouth."

The Duster cuffed him sharply on the side of the head. "Shut up, Morgan. Flanagan knew what he was doin'. You was drinkin' up all the profits."

The men laughed as Morgan protested plaintively. The Duster cried out, "Well, lads, we ain't goin' anyplace standin' here, jawin' about it, are we?"

"No!" they shouted.

"Let's go, then," The Duster cried. He lifted his musket and started a march downtown toward 42nd Street. A shouting mob fell in behind him. Women ran out of houses to join the procession. Young boys ran barefooted, stepping gingerly on the hot pavement. Only a few held their places at the barricades.

The mob turned west on 42nd Street and streamed on to the ferryhouse where the Weehawken boat docked, and to Flanagan's saloon.

They smashed into the saloon, driving out the bartenders and customers. Infuriated because Flanagan was not there, they began to destroy the place. Somehow, a fire started. The flames caught slowly, feeding on the long, mahogany bar, the oak paneled walls, the worn, comfortable chairs and the oak tables. They pillaged the saloon in a race against the flames. Men and women and little boys ran out into the street, arms laden with bottles of whisky. They drank and they jigged and hopped about in drunken glee.

The fire took hold and bright, flaming fingers curled out

through the shattered windows to reach up and catch the edges of the roof. Twisting strands of fire licked along the roof and wove together into lambent blazes.

The adjoining ferryhouse caught fire. The dried out wood of the ancient structure was quickly consumed by flames. And, all the while, the mob kept up an incessant din of shouting and cheering. Everyone was reeling drunk. Men shot pistols and muskets into the air. A drunken woman, suddenly berserk with whisky, leaped into the river screaming, "I have sinned! I have sinned!" She struggled briefly and sank, only to bob to the surface again floating slowly downstream on her face, her long hair spread out like strands of black seaweed.

At last the bacchanal spent itself. Slowly, they stumbled back to the barricaded streets. The taste of whisky was rancid in their mouths. They weaved and staggered. A young girl sat sprawled in a doorway, head lolling back, snoring drunkenly. Boys who had taken their first drinks vomited in the gutter.

The men who had rioted against an onerous law no longer could remember why they were out in the streets. The Draft had been forgotten and now only lawless depravity held the mob together.

An unnecessary delay held up the march against the mob's crude bastions. On West 35th Street, policemen stood waiting in formation outside the 20th Precinct station house. Slott's and Walling's men mobilized promptly, but the regulars under Wesson and the artillery pieces commanded by Major Watkins became enmeshed in the cumbersome protocol of military procedure.

At Police Headquarters, a long drum roll sent troops into line only to be dismissed while officers fussed with details. General Brown held an interminable council-of-war with company officers and gun commanders. Maps were unfolded. Routes of march were accepted only to be rejected. At the last moment, when the line-of-march had finally been agreed on, General Brown decided to hold inspection of the assembled troops.

He stalked by ranks of infantry, frowned at the guns and their gunners and fretted at this or that until almost an hour was lost. At last, he took a ceremonious departure and the order to march was given.

Caisson drivers cracked long whips, horses strained, and the field pieces rolled off on creaking wheels with gunners and crewmen sitting atop the limbers.

Infantry drummers beat out the step and the men moved off smartly. The enlisted men had endured the delays and the pompous strutting of their officers with resignation—to the private soldier it was merely the army way. They marched in well-dressed ranks, muskets at the right shoulder shift, and noted with sardonic humor that in spite of all the discussions and conferences the column was heading for West 35th Street by a complicated route going west on one block and east on another until the line of march resembled the twistings of a great snake.

Being soldiers, they went where ordered and did it in the prescribed manner. Sweat dripped down their faces and tunics grew dark with sweat. Full field packs weighted them down and the muskets felt like bars of heavy iron. After a bit, Captain Wesson gave the order to march at route step. Then, pipes were lighted, muskets were carried at every tilt.

The wily regulars made an arrangement with the ambulance driver who followed the column to carry their packs in his vehicle. Some tossed theirs onto the artillery limbers, hung them on fence pickets or threw them away. They were heading for a fight and in battle a man might legally claim he had lost his gear in action. If not, a knowing veteran could always steal another kit somewhere.

The column moved uptown, fieldpieces bouncing over poorly

paved streets. Being soldiers they grumbled about the heat, the city, their officers and the army—but as they swung along they sang heartily:

"Let the wide world wag as it will,
We'll be gay and happy still. . . ."

. . . 7

BY 6:00 P.M. the attack was ready to be mounted. Picked policemen were issued fire axes to hack through the barricades. They were to lead the assault backed by infantry and artillery. Fat, sweaty Major Watkins rushed his guns to the front when the column came into Ninth Avenue near 40th Street. The guns were shotted in full sight of the men crouching behind the barricades. A thin volley puffed out from the flimsy breastwork. Bullets splattered around the cannoneers. Watkins muttered a curse, spat tobacco juice and scowled blackly down the avenue.

"All right, boys. Let 'em have a sniff of grape. Number one gun, fire!" he said.

The snub-nosed cannon bounced with the report and cannoneers clung to the wheel spokes. The shell smashed into the barricades sending pieces of debris into the air. Men ran out from behind their wrecked fort. The second gun fired and grape whizzed up the avenue again.

Ragged volleys rained down from the roofs. The infantry deployed as skirmishers and opened up on the rooftop snipers and on riflemen shooting from the windows of houses. Window frames were splintered by bullets and panes of glass shattered. The ax-wielding police hacked a way through the first line of barricades. They were followed by squads of soldiers. Resistance was quickly overcome by bayonets, musket butts and locust sticks. Many of the rioters were so drunk they could put up only feeble resistance, but others fought desperately.

Chimneys were toppled into the street, the bricks bouncing on the pavement. The fieldpieces were hand-hauled up to the row of barricades that had been captured, and began to shell the next line behind which the rioters had fled for refuge.

Every time the gunners swabbed and reloaded their pieces, rioters popped up to shoot at them. The guns alone were not sufficient either to subdue the rioters or demolish the barricades. Men were needed for that work. The police captains, Walling and Slott, re-formed the storming parties and Captain Wesson's regulars made ready to continue the assault. A final barrage blasted from the cannon and the police charged forward in the face of a steady crackle of revolver and musket fire. The Metropolitans did not waver. Axes cut through wire bindings and splintered the crossbeams of the barricades. The troops streamed into the gaps. Another block had been captured, another barricade carried. The guns were rolled up to the new line and the hot and deadly job went on.

The fight was taking a heavy toll of the rioters. Bodies were lying in the wreckage of the breastworks and scattered along the sidewalks. Many rioters battled on gamely by sniping from the roofs and doorways or sneaking through back yards and over fences to fire at the rear of the attacking force.

But as barricades continued to be captured, patrols of regulars fanned out into the alleys and back passages and flushed out the isolated pockets of resistance. Ninth Avenue was a battlefield for almost two hours. Hand-to-hand fights raged. There were ugly clashes, the rioters relying on knives, clubs, fists or any weapon available against locust sticks, musket butts, and bayonets.

An end came to the fighting abruptly. Suddenly, there was no one for Walling and Slott and Wesson to attack. The rioters had faded into the gathering dusk and the avenue lay deserted.

The rioters fled singly and in groups. Hundreds ran to the riverbank to hide in the tall marsh grass or take refuge in squatters' shacks along the shore. Others concealed themselves in the attics and coalbins of houses on the side streets. Most ran aimlessly, hoping only to escape the cannon and the slashing bayonets.

There was no pursuit, the authorities satisfied to have broken up the mob concentration and the barricades. Major Watkins ordered his artillerymen to hitch up and soon the guns were ready to roll. Police details marched off to patrol the area, Walling's men turned east on 42nd Street, and Slott's covered the west side. The drummer boys, once more, beat out the long roll. The soldiers went into marching formation and headed back for Mulberry Street.

Ninth Avenue was quiet. A shocked silence covered the heat of the evening. Over to the west, the last streaks of crimson bloodied the sky beyond the Palisades. Complete darkness closed in at last, and doors began to open cautiously. The roadway was littered with debris and dead bodies. People moved furtively about in the wreckage flashing lanterns on the grisly scene. Dead men lay where they had fallen, some still clutching pistol or musket. Here and there, a woman was found lying where bullet or grapeshot had caught her. Behind one of the shattered barricades the searchers uncovered the corpse of a young woman. A man huddled beside her, sobbing.

During the night, the corpses were buried in dark places, in cellars or overgrown, rocky wasteland that ran to the riverbank.

The rioters cared for their wounded, too, and treated them with the help of a man who had once been a doctor. He patched them up as well as he could, pausing only to wipe his hands on a dirty, bloody towel and to take a pull at the bottle of whisky he kept beside him.

The street lights along the avenue were out of commission because the gas in the area had been cut off. Lanterns winked in the darkness. In scattered spots a pine torch threw off smoky sputtering light. Candles and kerosene lamps twinkled in windows. Order had been re-established on Ninth Avenue—but death and grief and hatred still lingered there.

Lamartine Place was a short block that connected West 28th and West 29th Streets between Eighth and Ninth Avenues. It was a pleasant spot with a few brownstone, high-stooped town houses. A gentle, scholarly man named Joseph Gibbons lived in such a house at 19 Lamartine Place. He became involved in the riots because Horace Greeley, his cousin, had once roomed in an upper floor of the place.

On the corner of Eighth Avenue and West 29th Street there was a grogshop, a grimy drinking place frequented mainly by Chelsea roughs. The neighborhood, once fashionable, was now turning into a decaying slum. The formerly well-kept houses had been allowed to fall into disrepair. Many owners had converted the brownstones into cheap rooming houses. What had been an area of middle-class gentility was invaded by hard-drinking, brawling dockworkers and poor laborers who lived under abominable conditions in crowded quarters.

Every once in a while Mr. Gibbons would consider selling his house and moving elsewhere, perhaps to rustic Westchester. But, even though the surrounding streets had suffered unfavorable change, Lamartine Place had remained unaltered, an island of respectability in a sea of deterioration.

Its houses were well kept and painted. Brasswork gleamed and the front yards were bright with flower beds. Gibbons and his neighbors chose to believe that the neighborhood would someday be restored to its former desirability.

The Gibbons house was comfortable and beautifully furnished with pieces from all over the world. The library contained many volumes bound in hand-wrought Moroccan leather, including rare first editions. The walls held fine paintings. Gibbons was a man of wealth and taste. A widower, he lived with two elderly spinster sisters, and owned a prosperous business dealing in objects of art. His customers included many of New York City's most distinguished families.

Fortunately, the old gentleman and his sisters were absent from the city on the fretful night of July 15th. Brawls had been breaking out all evening on West 28th Street and the residents of Lamartine Place kept their doors bolted and their shutters closed. Families huddled in parlors and the men armed themselves with shotguns and revolvers. A few times, bands of drunken rioters came through the quiet block but they had not yet given any trouble.

Those drinking in the grogshop on the corner were joined by many who had been in the fight on Ninth Avenue. They talked drunkenly about the rich residents on Lamartine Place and the treasures they owned. Women who had worked in the houses as domestics described the furniture, linens and silverware waiting to be looted.

Men listened slack-mouthed and red-eyed. The thought of looting pleased them. They shuffled restively, drunken stupor turning into viciousness. Someone said, "Damn it, why should they have so much and us have nothing?"

"Let's clean out the Gibbons place! That bastard Greeley is his cousin! He's no damn good!" a man cried.

"Aye, and I happen to know that Greeley lives in the house," a woman said.

"Why stop with Gibbons? Let's get 'em all!" a voice shouted.

Yelling wildly, they poured out of the saloon and started toward Lamartine Place in a howling mass. The mob boiled into the street. Rocks began to bounce off shuttered windows and to thud against doors. The rioters swirled over front gates and charged up the stoops. Suddenly, a shotgun blasted from an

upper window and pellets tore through the crowd. A revolver
spat flame and a woman fell dead. But nothing could stop the infuriated rioters now. Dozens of them charged up the steps of the
empty, undefended Gibbons house.

Once the rioters realized the house was unoccupied they attacked it from every side and managed to batter down the door.
Neighbors peered into the street cautiously and were relieved
to see the mob turn its main attention to plundering the Gibbons place.

Now that the way was open, screeching women dashed inside
to get their share of booty. They raced through rooms grabbing
anything that could be carried away. Shabby women carried
delicate Dresden figurines. Burly, illiterate men seized piles of
rare books. The house was ransacked from attic to basement and
the plunderers left a trail of wanton destruction. An antique
dressing table was splintered by a rioter who knocked it over
and jumped on it. Crystal chandeliers were ripped down from
the dining room and parlor ceilings. Priceless chinaware and
costly mirrors were smashed by the sweating vandals.

As the pillaging and havoc reached its peak, Captain James Z.
Bogart, 31st Precinct, and a detail of the Broadway Squad reinforced by several platoons of reserves, were out on a roving
patrol. The commotion attracted them and the police came into
West 28th Street on the double. Bogart, a rough-and-tumble
fighter, lost no time.

The men of the Broadway Squad were eager to pay the rioters back for the long fight around the State Armory, while the
officers from the 31st Precinct, located in the rural suburb of
Bloomingdale, had not yet been committed to action and were
raring to "see the elephant."

A flying wedge of husky policemen rammed into the mob.
Sticks thwacked heads and shoulders. Panic gripped the rioters
and while some fought with desperate terror the majority dropped
their loot and ran. At this point, the van of the infantry led by

Captain Wesson neared the scene. Upon hearing the uproar in the street, Wesson ordered a platoon ahead at the double. In the uncertain light of feeble street lamps, a jittery young officer, confused by the scuffling in the roadway and on the steps of the Gibbons house, bellowed a command to open fire.

A volley crackled down Lamartine Place. Bullets pelted the mass and struck rioters and policemen. An officer named Henry Dippel was hit in the thigh, the bullet tore into the bone and lodged in the marrow. The unlucky man suffered an agonized death a short time later in Jewish Hospital, 158 West 28th Street, a few blocks away. Six other policemen were also hospitalized for gunshot wounds, but recovered. Despite the tragic results of their intervention, the arrival of the troops ended the skirmish and rioters scattered in headlong retreat. Dozens were caught inside the house and subjected to a severe beating before being ejected. In this clash the women fought so fiercely that the police were forced to use their sticks on them, too.

Bogart left a strong guard on Lamartine Place and an uneasy quiet was maintained. As an aftermath to this fracas, an innocent passer-by was brutally beaten by a gang of disgruntled rioters who had escaped. The man happened to be walking down Eighth Avenue just when the last rioters were getting away. One of them pointed to him and yelled, "Get that son of a bitch! He's a reporter for *The Tribune!*"

A dozen men jumped him and left him horribly battered in a matter of seconds. They stole his watch, wallet, shoes and a stickpin. The unfortunate victim was not a newspaperman at all. He was a public schoolteacher who had returned only that evening from a vacation in the country.

. . . 8

MICHAEL DORGAN was an illiterate, twenty-three-year-old Irish immigrant who worked in Brown's Iron Factory on East 61st Street as a stoker. His job was to heave coal into the forge fires in which the ironsmiths and wroughters heated the metal they twisted into grilles and intricate scrolls to adorn the stoops and porches of the wealthy. For this tedious work, Dorgan received one dollar and fifty cents a day.

He was unmarried and lived in a pigsty of a room in a filthy tenement on West 22nd Street. He had been in New York City for five years and had come there from a little village in the north of Ireland, where the only home he had known was a thatched hut and the only food he could remember was thick, sour soup made from maggoty potatoes.

After his parents died in the bitter winter of '55 from the lung sickness, Dorgan left for America with his friend Jack Brayan. They had made their way to Liverpool where both got jobs aboard a packet boat bound for New York. Brayan had remained in New York only a brief time and then had headed out West, but Dorgan stayed on. His life was dull and brutish. He developed a squint from peering into the furnace fireboxes ten hours a day, six days a week. The heat had wizened his skin and given him the appearance of an old man. His only relief from the monotony of work came on Saturday nights when he went to Paradise Square with other workingmen to drink beer and try to find a whore. The young, pretty ones would not go with him and he could not have afforded them, anyway. He had to be satisfied with the weary whores no one else wanted. But he accepted that, too, as part of his warped and dismal existence.

During the five years in New York City, Dorgan had known only misery—and he had learned to hate. First, he hated wealthy people. Once in a while, on sun-bright Sundays, he would walk the streets and come onto Fifth Avenue to stare with awe and dull smoldering resentment at the elegant mansions, the carriages, the sleek creamy-white women who were dressed in shiny satin and wore glittering jewelry. He sometimes dared to peep into the windows of the houses and glimpsed the luxurious parlors of burnished wood, the plush furniture. He saw these things and seethed without understanding his rage. And he would walk down Broadway to stand at the shop windows, to glance into hotel lobbies or linger at the kitchen entrance of a restaurant and sniff the aroma of foods he had never tasted in a world he could never enter.

Once he had walked very far downtown and on the corner of Catherine and Ann Streets he came to the grand Brooks Brothers store. He stared for a long time into the display window at the array of suits and hats and gleaming leather shoes. The shoes fascinated him. A pair of shoes like those, he believed, were even worth a man's soul. He yearned for such shoes and would sit in his cell of a room wondering how it must feel to wear them. The only shoes he owned were the broken, scarred boondockers—misshapen work shoes.

Second, he hated Negroes. Dorgan did not know why he should hate them. But at Brown's the men all despised the "dirty niggers." The workers expressed such animosity against them that Dorgan, who didn't even know any Negroes and never had spoken to one, also hated them. He had seen Negroes of course. But those who worked on the docks or in factories seemed no different from the white men who did the same jobs except that their skins were black. But because the others hated them, Dorgan did, too. That was his life. He ate, slept, worked, drank beer, had a sagging whore once in a while, hated the rich and hated the Negroes.

The war brought little change to Dorgan. He still worked as a stoker at Brown's and cast gun mounts instead of grilles. He labored longer hours and received a few dollars more a week. Dorgan did not know what the war was about and he did not care. Sometimes, soldiers paraded on the street with bands playing and people cheering. That was the war.

On Monday, July 13, he had reported for work as usual at 7:00 A.M. The workers of Brown's were all gathered outside in front of the factory gate on East 61st Street. They were very excited and kept yelling, "No work! To hell with the Draft!"

Dorgan remembered that some months before a man had come to the factory and asked him and the other workers to give their names which he wanted to write down in a big book. The workers became very angry with him and would not give their names. They told Dorgan it was for a draft to put men in the army and ship them off to war. They told him that was no good and he believed them because he knew nothing of such things.

The men swore nobody would take them to the army without a fight and Dorgan said the same, never really comprehending exactly what was going on. He was an organism encrusted in a shell of ignorance, poverty and brutishness, one of thousands like himself in the great city.

He had not worked on Monday but had gone with the rest to Central Park and then down to the Provost Marshal's office. When the fighting started, Dorgan had tried to run away, but was hemmed in by the mob and so could not escape. He was swept along, running and shouting like all the others. He drank freely until there was no reality. Everything around him seemed to be happening in a haze and he went from one place to another through a fog of whisky and fire, like a piece of driftwood carried in a stormy sea.

He could remember little of the previous night except that a rainstorm had pelted the city and he was with men in a smoky grogshop gulping food someone had given him, drinking more whisky and feeling a sense of power he had never before experienced. This was the way to live: rushing aimlessly along strange streets, breaking into houses, setting fires. He slept on the dirty floor of a saloon and was sick from the whisky.

And with daylight it had started all over again. No work. Nothing to do but roam the streets and sometimes, to run from the police. He took part in many fights; the soldiers had come with cannon. It had been terrible. All around him, people were killed. He even saw a man's head get blown off by a charge of shot from a cannon. He ran then and was caught up in another mob. They had whisky. He drank. He roved with them and daylight faded.

The men he had joined kept on the move. They prowled without purpose and then they came to a place that was familiar to Dorgan. He found himself staring drunkenly into the Brooks Brothers' window on Catherine Street. He pressed close to the glass and blinked at the rows of shoes on display. The shoes. He wanted shoes like those.

Someone yelled, "There's clothing in there for all. Let's go get it!"

A brick crashed through the show window. Men climbed in and there was a mass scramble to get into the store. More windows were knocked out. The mob flooded the store. Rioters climbed over counters, grabbing armloads of shirts, neckties, suits, anything that could be stolen. Dorgan was shoved inside the place. The ground floor was a bedlam of shrieking, laughing men and women who struggled with one another over the division of the spoils. Two men tugged at a pair of trousers, each pulling on a leg. They yanked until the garment tore in half and each tumbled over still clutching a trouser leg.

A rioter discovered the valve that controlled the gaslight and turned on the illumination. The fixtures lit an incredible scene. A drunken woman was doing a jig atop a counter. She wore a plug hat and waved a silken shirt like a flag. The stairways leading to the upper floors were packed with people squirming and shoving and carrying piles of suits, underwear, socks and shirts.

Somehow Dorgan made his way to an upper floor. He came to a counter where dozens of pairs of shoes were on display. They were the finest shoes made of cordovan leather and calfskin and the leather shone darkly in the gaslight. All about him, men were cramming themselves into trousers, pulling one pair on top of another and draping the suit jackets over their arms. Others dashed about wildly pulling clothing from the racks and snatching up whole bolts of material. A man rushed by with three hats on his head, one pressed onto the other. A woman dragged a gunnysack bulging with wearing apparel. But Dorgan did none of these things. He stood by the shoe counter feasting his eyes on the footwear. At last he reached out timidly and let his fingers rest on a shoe for only an instant. The leather was even softer than he had imagined. After a while, he picked up a pair of shoes and held them tightly to his chest.

He tried to walk out of the place then, with his treasure. He kept glancing at the shoes, not yet able to believe they were actually in his possession. He could not get to the stairs because the press of people was too great. And all at once there was an outburst from the mob in the street outside the building. A warning cry went up, "The coppers! The coppers are coming!" Those on the upper floors rushed to the windows and cried out in dismay. A cordon of police was closing in. Even from two stories above street level they could hear the police clubs thudding. The pillagers tried to escape but suddenly the Metropolitans were everywhere. They struck down rioters without giving quarter. Those not lucky enough to avoid the locust sticks were beaten unconscious. Women did not escape the fury of the police and were hurled bodily down the stairs. Dozens of rioters were stretched insensible at the foot of the stairs. Some did manage to get away and hang on to their loot but for most, the punishment was swift and sure in the shape of a stout locust stick.

Dorgan ran to the rear of the store near a bank of windows. He still held the shoes. A burly policeman, brandishing a club, came toward him. Dorgan screamed in terror, and driven by fear to unreasoning action, he leaped headfirst through the window. He landed on the pavement and his neck broke with a loud snap. He was clinging to the shoes in his death grip when the morgue wagon came to take his body.

At midnight, a telegram was handed to Mayor Opdyke. He read it at a glance and a smile lit up his tired face. Opdyke showed the message to Acton. The commissioner read:

Washington, July 14th, 1863

To the Hon. George Opdyke,
Mayor, New York City

Sir:

Five regiments are under orders to return to New York. The retreat of Lee now becomes a rout, with his army broken and much heavier loss of killed and wounded than was supposed. This will relieve a large force for the restoration of order in New York.

Edwin M. Stanton
Secretary of War

When Acton had read it, Opdyke went to Governor Seymour who was in conversation with General Brown. He read the telegram aloud to the men.

The Governor expressed his relief and Brown said, "Now we'll show those rebel bastards a few things."

Word spread quickly through the busy room. The telegraphers cheered and applauded. Policemen on duty tossed their caps to the ceiling. Soldiers camped in the street heard the news and jubilation spread from rank to rank. Even the sentries cheered the welcome tidings. The exuberance spread to the Negro refugees who shouted and clapped their hands.

Acton leaned against the table. His eyes were burning with weariness. "Thank God," he whispered fervently.

Wednesday
July 15, 1863

. . . 1

NIGHT dragged interminably in the apprehensive city. Terror crept the deserted streets. Every shadow was an object of monstrous dread. The night passed slowly; humid and hot. Damp mists clung tenaciously along the riverbanks while lightning flickered and thunder grumbled like the querulous growling of an old dog.

In many neighborhoods there were no street lights, for the riot had kept workers from operating the gas plants. No friendly lights showed in windows. Doors were barred, windows closed and shutters drawn. In the wealthier sections of the city men with weapons ready stayed awake and peered into the curtained darkness. Nothing was moving in the streets except the alley cats scrounging in garbage heaps.

Men guarded their homes with cocked pistols and waited for the morning like sentries on picket duty in enemy territory. Women sat up with their men, masking fright and worry by pretending to knit or to read but furtively eyeing their cherished belongings and remembering the fearful reports of what had happened during the last awful days. Less than forty-eight hours had passed since the beginning of the riot but to the embattled people of New York it seemed an eternity.

The city awaited daylight and its people wondered when there would be relief from the horror that had befallen them.

At 4:30 A.M., while the waning night was still clinging to the darkness, a hackney carriage pulled away from Police Headquarters, rolling past soldiers sleeping on the sidewalk. Sentries leaning on bayoneted muskets glanced casually at the carriage and the two men seated in the driver's box. The men, dressed in nondescript civilian clothes, were James Crowley, Chief of the Police Telegraphic Bureau, and his second in command, Eldred Polhamus. Disguised as hackney drivers, they were going out along Third Avenue to inspect the telegraph wires.

With Crowley holding the reins, they drove uptown, moving slowly, as Polhamus flashed his bull's-eye lantern and looked for broken wires. On occasion, they stopped to make a quick repair. One stood guard with drawn revolver, while the other worked by the lantern light.

No one interfered with them and, in fact, they saw no one. Third Avenue was like a street in a ghost city. The bleak, charred remains of the Provost Marshal's office and the gutted tenements were gaunt specters brooding over their fate. The litter of the battle still cluttered the streets from 40th Street north to 47th Street. Deserted streetcars whose broken windows gaped like blinded eyes blocked the tracks. The lots between Third Avenue and Lexington Avenue were like mysterious wastelands and the partially finished buildings loomed as grotesque hulks.

Crowley and Polhamus drove by this place where the city's agonies had commenced and continued along Third Avenue until they came to the edge of Jones' Woods. By then, the pale light of dawn had eased the darkness. The woodland was a formless mass from which came the twittering and chirping of numberless birds. Off toward the misty river a rooster crowed, then another, and crimson streaks of sunlight tipped the leaden sky.

"We'd better head back, Eldred," Crowley said.

Polhamus nodded. He was a taciturn man who had an in-credible knowledge of telegraphy. As he turned the horse for the return trip, Crowley smiled. Polhamus was known to remain silent for days on end and some of his brother officers had never even heard his voice. But a repairman did not have to be a con-versationalist, and Polhamus was one of the best repairers Crow-ley had ever met.

They jogged down Third Avenue, moving more quickly, now. As the daylight grew stronger, small crowds began gathering on street corners. They stood in ragged clusters without spirit or animation, dull-eyed and lumpish people who had done too much drinking the night before.

As the policeman approached 34th Street, they saw four men huddled together on the corner. Two of the men stepped into the roadway flourishing revolvers and signaled Crowley to halt the hackney. He sawed on the reins and stopped the horse.

"My pals and me want a ride to Water Street," one of the men said.

The policemen exchanged glances. Polhamus winked and nodded.

"Then climb aboard, lads," Crowley cried cheerfully.

The men piled into the carriage. Each had a revolver thrust into his belt and each was pretty drunk. They were dirty and unkempt and the man who had spoken to Crowley had dried blood smeared across his face. He poked his head out the win-dow and shouted up to Crowley, "Now then, bucko, feed your nag the whip and we'll make it worth your while."

"Yes, sir, gentlemen," Crowley said, cracking the whip.

The horse was a good one and stretched his legs. The carriage rocked and jounced flinging the men about inside the vehicle. Polhamus clung to the handholds of the driver's box while Crow-ley stood up, snapping the whip and urging the horse to greater speed. They rattled wildly down rutted Third Avenue and into the Bowery. At Bleecker Street, Crowley made a sharp turn and pulled up at Police Headquarters. The carriage had barely stopped rolling when Polhamus vaulted from his seat and yanked the door open, his revolver leveled at the shaken passengers.

He jerked a thumb over his shoulder indicating they should get out. Crowley covered them from the other side, revolver ready. Soldiers crowded about and policemen hustled over. The passengers stood white-faced and with hands raised. "What's all this? We ain't done nothin'," one of them whined.

"Shut up," Crowley snapped. He turned to a policeman in the group. "Delaney, please escort these gentlemen inside and have Mr. Hawley register them in our guest book."

The policeman grinned, "Yes, sir."

"And, Delaney, introduce them to Sergeant Young. He'll enjoy chatting with such fine gentlemen," Crowley said.

"Yes, Mr. Crowley," Delaney said. He nudged the man nearest him with his locust stick. "Get a move on, Johnny Roach."

"You're makin' a mistake, officer," the man said.

"Listen, mister—get moving or I'll ram this stick down your gullet. I've had my fill of you people," Delaney said.

The prisoners moved without any further protest. Delaney followed them up the steps and into the building. Crowley turned to Polhamus. "Well, Eldred, the next time those fellows hail a hack, they'll make sure who's sitting in the driver's seat," he said.

A smile grew on Polhamus' dour face. It became a grin and then he burst into peal after peal of long-bottled-up laughter. Crowley started to laugh too and the infectiousness of it spread to the soldiers and the police. Gasping for breath and dabbing at his eyes, Polhamus said, "You should have seen their faces when I opened the door and shoved the pistol at them. They looked like maiden ladies caught in an outhouse." He began laughing again, leaning against the hack for support.

The sun had been up barely an hour when it was obvious that

the day was going to be a scorcher. An overcast hung above the city and the sun was a burning ember beating through the layer of clouds. The air seemed to have been sucked through a gigantic furnace. It was a day when mongrel dogs lay panting in the shade and the rivers flowed with mirror perfect surfaces unruffled by the slightest breeze. The heat crushed down on the close-packed tenements, turning each room into an oven of torment. The sail ships dotting the harbor rode anchor with stern flags limp on their poles and pennons hanging motionless from the mainmast halyard.

With sulky reluctance, the city stirred into listless activity. An omnibus of the Sixth Avenue line started uptown from Vesey Street but a band of fifty rioters stoned the conveyance at Carmine Street. The driver promptly turned around and brought his vehicle back to the depot at top speed. No further attempt was made to run public cars on the city's streets.

However, ferry service between New York and Brooklyn returned to comparative normalcy. Although few passengers were commuting into the city, the outbound traffic was heavy. Ferry slips were jammed with frightened New Yorkers, including many Negroes, heading for Brooklyn. And at the earliest morning hours reports came into Headquarters that the swamps and woodlands of the Eastern District were filled with Negro refugees. In one isolated wooded place, young Negro men dug rifle pits and set up a camp for escapees, patrolled by armed guards.

But not only Negroes were fleeing the city. Carriages with liveried drivers and footmen rolled out of the fashionable districts carrying wealthy families toward Westchester. It was a commonplace sight to see crowded vehicles racing headlong up the Bloomingdale Road, trailing dust, passengers clinging to hand straps, the horses heaving and slavering.

And violence soon showed itself again in brutal, snarling outbursts. . . .

. . . 2

MORNING newspapers were published in offices where reporters scratched out copy with loaded revolvers close by. Printers worked in composing rooms which had been turned into small arsenals and a musket stood by every printers' stone.

But despite the lurid turbulence, one optimistic note appeared in the papers. Cheered by the telegram from Stanton, Mayor Opdyke issued a proclamation which was carried by the newspapers:

PROCLAMATION BY THE MAYOR!

July 15, 1863

To All Citizens of New York:

I am happy to announce to you that the riot which for two days has disgraced our city, has been in good measure subjected to the control of public authorities. What now remains of the mob are fragments prowling about for plunder and for the purpose of meeting these you are invited to form voluntary associations under competent leaders to patrol and guard your districts. With these exceptions you are requested to resume your accustomed daily vocations.

George Opdyke, Mayor.

Shortly after daybreak, Opdyke's wishful proclamation was belied, as the first brutal act of disorder exploded. Ann Derrickson, a white woman, was married to a Negro. It had been a quiet life although she had been the target of gibes by her neighbors on York Street for all the twelve years of her marriage.

When the rioting began, her husband, a seaman, was away on a voyage. For two days, Mrs. Derrickson had stayed in the small tidy house with her eleven-year-old son. But, on Wednesday morning, she decided to emigrate to Brooklyn. At an early hour she packed a carpetbag with extra clothing and a little food, and with her son, slipped out of the house and headed for the Brooklyn ferry. But as she started to go along the street a group of her neighbors, housewives, gathered in a menacing group.

"There she is, the nigger's whore!" a woman screeched.

The shrieking woman rushed at her. The others joined in the attack. They clawed at Ann Derrickson with hatred that stemmed from fear. She had dared to defy society by entering a marriage of miscegenation and this made her different. They had nothing in their drab lives except the threadbare wrappings of respectability. They were married to drunkards, brawlers—they lived in poverty and filth. Their children were sickly and undernourished and they, themselves, were coarsened, hard, ugly. But because they had married men of the same race they cloaked themselves in smug probity. And with the intolerance that only the righteous can mobilize, they believed this gave them license to destroy those who did not conform.

Ann Derrickson was the scapegoat of their virtuous wrath. They knocked her down and trampled her until she was unconscious. Her son cowered on the stoop screaming in terror. A snaggle-toothed harridan, who had been beating the mother with a stick, pointed to the boy and cried, "Kill the nigger's whelp! Kill him!"

The women turned from their battered and dying victim and glared at the boy. He was a slight, brown-skinned lad with great liquid brown eyes in a thin, pointed face like that of a wistful fox. The women's eyes glowed with the madness of bigotry and there was no mercy on their faces.

Now, the boy became the object of their unreasoning frenzy. They went for him with shrill curses and clawing hands. Somehow, he managed to evade them and ran away. They chased him for a bit, then limited the pursuit to futile fist shaking as he darted around the corner.

Angered by the boy's escape, the women gathered around Ann Derrickson and pelted her to death with stones.

A telegram notified Police Headquarters that a mob of six or seven thousand were out lynching Negroes in the vicinity of Eighth Avenue and 32nd Street. Fortunately, a strong force of cavalry under Colonel Thaddeus Mott had completed a patrol and was awaiting orders in Mulberry Street. Acton informed Brown of the situation uptown and the old soldier ordered Mott to break up the mob.

Cavalry bugles sounded and in a few minutes the troop was riding hell-for-leather with two pieces of artillery bumping along in the rear of the column. At precisely 9:00 A.M. Colonel Mott's command arrived at Eighth Avenue and 32nd Street. The big mob was in a wild mood. It had concentrated around a lamppost from which the mutilated bodies of three Negroes dangled. As the cavalry came into view, bugles blaring, red guidons fluttering, the mob spread out defiantly. The horsemen formed into attack formation. Sabers flashed from scabbards. Mott ordered the artillerymen to set up their pieces and this was promptly done. The mob, a bit awed by this display of military efficiency, dropped back a little. Mott spurred his horse through the front ranks of the crowd and with a slash of his saber cut down one of the hanging Negroes.

A rioter reached up and tried to pull him from the saddle. The Colonel struck out with his saber and split the man's skull. Not deigning a backward glance, Mott turned his horse and galloped back to his men.

The mob was stunned by the suddenness of the action. Those close by stared aghast at the man Mott had struck down. The rioter had fallen close to the body of the hanged Negro, who had been a hunchback. The mob was indecisive for only a few moments. The rioters started flinging rocks at the troopers and shooting at them with pistols. The bullets zinged about the cavalrymen, all seasoned veterans who were not fazed by the gunfire.

Colonel Mott rose up in his stirrups and pointed his saber at the mob which had begun to advance. "Disperse, or I'll open fire with the cannon," he cried.

The answer came in jeers and catcalls followed by a hail of rocks and more indiscriminate firing from the mob. The cavalrymen kept a tight rein on their restive horses and eyed the oncoming horde. A bullet almost whipped Mott's hat from his head. He spurred his mount to the artillery officer and cried, "Don't wait another moment, Captain Howell! Open fire!"

Howell glanced at the mob. "Yes, sir," he said and saluted. He was glad of the order. If the Colonel had waited any longer the mob would have been on them and then the fancy cavalry boys would have had a mess on their hands. A long-time artillerist, Howell had contempt for every branch of the service except his own. To him the cavalry was suitable only for delivering messages and dashing about without purpose.

Howell did not see his target as human beings. Every target presented the same problem: so much range at so much elevation required so much powder to score a hit. He gave his orders to the cannoneers and the guns spat flame one after the other. Grapeshot ripped into the oncoming mass and the mob shuddered like a wounded beast. Yet, it did not break up in spite of the wailing cries of the wounded and the grisly slug-riddled dead staring sightlessly in the misty glare of the summer sun.

Again the guns fired and the pellets swooshed by like gentle whispers. This time the mob was stricken and even the cries of the wounded were drowned by screams of terror as the rioters fled. The street was filled from one curbstone to the other with frantic, panic-stricken people trying to escape the guns. A cloud of black gunpowder smoke moved in lazy eddies over the heads of the struggling mass.

Colonel Mott's saber twinkled in a downward flash of steel. A bugler sounded the urgent blare of the charge, and yelling troopers waving heavy sabers dug spurs into the flanks of eager horses whose flaring nostrils had sniffed the familiar odor of gunpowder. The rows of horsemen drove into the mob behind the guidons and pennons fluttering bright crimson—brighter even than the blood which stained the cobblestones as the riders slashed and hacked through the mob.

It was over in minutes. The bugler blew retreat. The troopers re-formed in disciplined ranks, young faces florid under the peaks of jaunty cavalry kepis. Colonel Mott, his eyes shadowed by the broad brim of his gold-braided slouch hat, looked up the avenue. Only the dead and wounded remained where the mob had been. The two lynched Negroes swayed slowly to and fro. A cavalry sergeant cut the ropes and the bodies dropped to the ground. Having no facilities to care for the wounded, Mott wasted no time on them despite the chorus of agonized groans. His men rode slowly after him back to Police Headquarters.

The mob had the last word, however—and in a sense, the victory. After the cavalry departed rioters returned to carry away their dead and wounded. With defiant fury they strung up the Negroes to the very tree from which they had been cut down and the mutilated bodies dangled grotesquely—blameless sacrifices to unbridled hatred.

One of the lynched men was a gentle hunchback named Abraham Franklin. He was barely twenty years old but his face was puckered and drawn and old with suffering. He had been sickly as a child and stricken by a disease that had twisted his back and deformed his body. But his arms were strong and he was quick and intelligent. He worked as a coachman for a wealthy family on Madison Square and lived in a comfortable room over the mews adjoining the great town house. Abraham was a skilled driver and had a way with horses, so in spite of his appearance he was a desirable coachman.

For the past two days, his employer had forbidden him to go out into the street and had insisted that he stay in the big house where he would be safe. All male servants had been given arms and the house, with shutters drawn and doors barred, was an imposing fortress.

Mobs had rampaged nearby and the people in the embattled mansion were aware of the destruction. For two days, Abraham had remained safely behind the locked doors, worrying about his mother, a widow, who lived alone in a shanty on West 32nd Street. He thought about her constantly and at last, on Wednesday morning, could stand the anxiety no longer. He told his employer that he must look after her. The householder understood Abraham's distress. He told the coachman to get his mother and bring her back with him. He urged Abraham to take a pistol, but the hunchback refused the weapon. A side door was opened and he slipped out into the stableyard. He hitched a horse to a light buggy and drove to his mother's shanty.

He reached her place unmolested and was pleased to find her unharmed. Abraham told his mother to gather up a few belongings and come with him. She was starting to pack when bands of shouting men appeared on the block. They set fire to some shanties across the street. Abraham and his mother knew they were trapped. Facing each other, they knelt to pray. They had just begun to recite the Lord's Prayer when the mob kicked down the door of the shanty.

WEDNESDAY morning found the prosperous and usually thriving business section of Grand Street with shuttered shops and deserted sidewalks. But as the morning passed without any hint of trouble, some shopkeepers regained confidence. They reasoned that Mayor Opdyke must know what he was about to have issued his proclamation that the rioters were under control.

The shop owners took down shutters, rolled up awnings and unlocked doors.

Morris L. Bryant kept a hat and cap store at 468 Grand Street. On the corner, at Willet and Grand, Max Silverstein owned a clothing store. Next door to him was Hyman Hershberger's shirt shop. Duncan Fowler sold shoes at 464 Grand Street and on the same block were a tobacconist's, a millinery shop and a hoop skirt store. It was a street of small independent merchants—solid citizens whose businesses symbolized to them the freedom they enjoyed in a free nation. These shopkeepers were men of divergent backgrounds. Some were native born, others had come as immigrants fleeing from the revolutions and counterrevolutions that had swept Central Europe. None would ever attain the affluence of a Rowland Macy or an A. T. Stewart, but their shops brought a comfortable living; each man would have something to hand over to his children.

Customarily, the merchants of Grand Street closed their doors only on July 4th, Christmas Day, New Year's Day and Sundays. But the first two days of rioting had brought business to a halt. Rumors created panic that spread with epidemic speed. Mobs had raged back and forth through the area but this part of Grand Street had been left unscathed, although there had been some shooting between rioters and Marines on Pitt and Stanton Streets only a few blocks away early on Tuesday.

According to the Mayor, the danger was over and the merchants were prepared to do business as usual. Morris Bryant, forty-eight years old, was busily rearranging his stock of hats and caps when a gang of men came into his store. The leader, a lean young man, stared silently at Bryant while his followers ranged themselves behind him, grinning like evil children.

Bryant was a small man, but made up for his lack of height by his resolute and dignified bearing. He saw the men had been drinking and knew they were out for mischief, but he hid his fear and confronted them with apparent calm.

"May I help you, gentlemen?" he asked politely.

The young leader walked to him and glanced about the store. His men snickered and nudged each other waiting for the next move.

The man said, "My name's Jeremy Turner. And I think you should give my pals and me nice new hats as presents. What do you think of that, bucko?"

Bryant moistened his dry lips. A vagrant ray of sunlight filtered through the shop window and glinted off the merchant's eyeglasses. He did not speak.

Turner's hand shot out and his open palm cracked sharply across Bryant's cheek. The blow knocked the eyeglasses to the floor and shattered them. Bryant gasped but made no move to fight back. With a sneer, Turner said to his men, "Help yourselves, lads. Mr. Bryant's givin' with a free hand. Now, ain't you, Bryant?"

Bryant made no reply and his silence seemed to infuriate the gangster. He knocked the shopkeeper down with a punch. Bryant lay on the floor, clenching his teeth to keep from crying out. He screwed his eyes tightly shut so as not to see the men tearing open hat boxes and hurling expensive beavers down and trampling on them. At last, the vandalism ended. Turner said, "Let's go, lads."

The men trooped out, laughing and shoving each other, putting fists through hat crowns, heaving a glass showcase over and scaling bowlers into the gutter. Turner bent over Bryant and said, "Listen, you little Jew bastard, we're coming back in two hours and we'll do worse if you don't shell out five hundred dollars. We'll burn your damn store down and tear you apart. You hear?"

Then, he was gone. Bryant dragged himself to his feet. He stood shaking, staring at the wreckage of his shop. The rioters visited other stores—Hirshberger's and Silverstein's and Fowler's —every shop on the block, and they went away, arms filled with stolen goods. They wrecked each store and warned each merchant they wanted five hundred dollars on their return visit.

The shopkeepers held a meeting. They were scared, but determined not to pay and they looked into each other's bruised faces and gathered strength from one another.

Bryant had a brother-in-law who was a volunteer fireman in Engine Company Number 17. He went to the firehouse and told his story. The volunteers rallied around him and armed themselves with spanners and wrenches and ax handles and hid themselves in Bryant's storeroom.

When Turner and his henchmen came back the volunteers came out and beat them. The roughs fled, but the shopkeepers got their revenge. They ganged up on Turner until he begged on his knees for mercy. Because they were peace-loving men they let him stagger away, knowing the bully would never bother them again.

Trains loaded with troops chugged toward New York through the green, rain-drenched farmlands of Pennsylvania. The soldiers sat in the cars gripping muskets tightly and thinking about the tumultuous situation in New York City. They had read elaborate reports of what was happening there in the newspapers and were heading home with the emotions of men moving to attack a hostile city.

The young soldiers who had seen their first battle at Gettysburg were tense and worried, fearful for the safety of their families and friends. The veterans, hardened and cynical after two years of war, amused themselves by teasing the recruits, spreading alarming rumors and making up wild stories about the riot.

The train rocked up through the countryside and the men fretted and argued, played cards and dice, slept, sang and tried to shake off thoughts filled with foreboding. Sparks flew from the locomotive's stack. The sweating fireman fed wood into the raging maw of the firebox and the engineer, squinting into the afternoon sun, edged the throttle to the last notch. He wanted those soldiers to be in New York at the earliest moment. His wife and kids were there and he was worried about them. He cursed the miles that seemed to stretch ahead interminably.

• • • *4*

THE weary men of the police force and the exhausted soldiers still had work to do. No matter how hard they smashed one mob, another appeared, and Wednesday was marked by a succession of bloody fights. Commissioner Acton, drawn and gaunt, with dark circles under his eyes, stood on the steps of Headquarters and watched a police detail marching out to break up a mob that was forming for another attack on the

Negro quarter. He waved at the men and shouted, "Go on, boys! Go on! Give it to them, now! Quail on toast for every man of you as soon as the mob is put down! Quail on toast, boys!"

Fatigued as they were, the policemen laughed and managed to raise a hoarse cheer. Their fighting spirit was not dampened. But some members of the Board of Aldermen and the City Council were not as courageous. They called an emergency meeting and the political hacks, mindful that the rioters also were voters, did not have the best interests of the city at heart.

A quorum being present, the legislative bodies voted to appropriate two million five hundred thousand dollars to pay the exemption of any future draftee who could not pay the three hundred dollars himself. Having passed this cowardly bill without debate and in undignified haste, the worthy Aldermen and Council men adjourned. A delegation of them went to Police Headquarters to present a petition to Opdyke and Seymour requesting that they stop using force against "the people gathered to protest the odious and despotical Draft Law."

Unfortunately for them, they ran into General Brown who was in a bad mood. A detachment of his troops had been roundly defeated in an uptown street and had fled in disorder. The report had just arrived and Brown was in no humor to be crossed. On seeing the deputation of politicians, Brown demanded their business. When they told him, he dropped his hand to his sword hilt and roared, "Get out of here you meddling bastards before I clap the whole rotten crew of you into Fort Lafayette!"

One glance at his purple face and wild eyes was enough. The politicians left and didn't return.

Uptown, the situation had become critical again, especially along First Avenue between 18th and 19th Streets. Mackerelville toughs and segments of mobs from all over had joined forces in that vicinity. This was the mob that had overwhelmed Brown's soldiers. Now, they were roistering through the streets with captured trophies—muskets, swords, pistols and even a small cannon. No ammunition was available for the fieldpiece but to the rioters it represented a great triumph merely to have gained its possession.

In the brownstone house at 202 East 19th Street, pretty Ellen Leonard of Boston, on a visit to her aunt, peered from the window of an upstairs room and watched the raucous mob cavorting below. Julia Morse's son had rejoined his regiment and the two women had been trapped alone in the house for two days. On this third day of their ordeal, they were thoroughly frightened. For the first time since the rioting had started the mob was looting houses in the neighborhood, and only that morning a girl had been raped and murdered in Stuyvesant Park.

On learning this terrible news from a neighbor who had ventured out, Julia Morse had decided it was time she and Ellen went to Police Headquarters for their own safety. The mob had burned the precinct house on East 22nd Street the night before and the best sanctuary was Mulberry Street. But it was too late. No one could have gone through the agitated crowds in the neighborhood. Convinced they could not leave, Julia had climbed up to the attic that very morning and after rummaging about in a trunk had come downstairs carrying a loaded revolver.

"This belonged to your uncle and he taught me to use it. I'll not let those ruffians harm you, Ellen," she said, drawing her lips into a tight line.

General Brown dispatched Colonel Cleveland Winslow with a 150-man force from mixed commands, supported by a two-gun battery commanded by Colonel E. E. Jardine of Hawkins' Zouaves, to break up the mobs terrorizing the First Avenue district.

The infantry went into a skirmish line at the corner of 18th

Street and First Avenue and prepared to engage the rioters. But the mob members had learned something of tactics in fighting the soldiers during the past few days. Snipers on roofs kept up a steady fire, which the troops could not quash.

General Brown had made a grievous mistake by committing the troops without an accompanying force of police. Locust sticks and revolvers were needed to clear the rooftops, not clumsy muskets. In other clashes the soldiers had been effective only when supported by police clubs. The outnumbered infantrymen could not reload and fire quickly enough to sweep the roofs, and the unwieldy muskets were useless for fighting in narrow hallways and on staircases.

As the soldiers began crumpling under the sniper fire, men in the mob opened with firearms from the street. Colonel Jardine ordered his guns unlimbered. But again the mob foiled the soldiers. As the guns were being readied for action, the rioters leaped into doorways or flung themselves prostrate to the paving stones and the grapeshot whistled harmlessly up the avenue.

While the guns were being reloaded, the armed rioters stepped out again and fired quick volleys, ducking to safety when the cannon spat grape. After a few minutes, about half of the military force had been disabled, and a number of soldiers killed. Seeing the futility of keeping up this fight, Winslow ordered a withdrawal.

Colonel Jardine was supervising the limbering up of his guns when a rioter stepped into the middle of the street, took deliberate aim and shot the officer in the thigh. A soldier killed the man a moment later.

The mob, seeing that the troops were ready to pull out went after them in a wild, frenzied charge. The attack was so savage that the soldiers broke in complete defeat, abandoning their dead and wounded. The caisson drivers lashed up the horses and rocketed away, leaving Colonel Jardine behind. The wounded officer managed to crawl under an upended wagon where he was joined by two soldiers, one of whom had been hit in the arm. The men dragged Jardine into East 19th Street through an alleyway during the confusion of the mob's assault.

The street was temporarily devoid of rioters who had joined in the charge on the troops. The two soldiers held Jardine erect and looked about wondering where they might find a refuge. Dusk was closing in and the fading light helped them for the few moments they needed.

Ellen Leonard and her aunt, watching from the window, saw the men. Aunt Julia, taking in the situation at a glance, dashed downstairs, closely followed by Ellen. She unlocked the front door and called to the soldiers, "Quickly, in here. Come in here!"

The men aided Jardine up the steps and into the house. Ellen slammed the door shut and slid the bolt. The soldiers stood in the hallway breathing hard. Colonel Jardine, his face ashen, blood soaking his trousers whispered, "Thank you, madam. You are very kind."

"Never mind the politeness," Julia said. "There's no time for that. Get him upstairs, into the attic. Ellen, show them the way. That mob may be back any moment."

The soldiers half-carried Jardine up the stairs, following Ellen. She lit the old kerosene lamp in the attic and the men placed the officer on a sagging couch. One of the men slashed the Colonel's trouser leg with a clasp knife and looked at the wound, beckoning Ellen to bring the light closer. She obeyed, turning her head not to see the blood. For a moment, she felt faint and her knees buckled. The soldier with the arm wound leaped to her side and steadied her, encircling her waist with his good arm. She leaned against him weakly.

"Are you all right, miss?" he asked.

"Yes. Thank you." She moved away from him, blushing. "You'd best look after the Colonel—and—and yourself. I'm sorry to have been such a ninny."

"Ah, the sight of blood's enough to turn anyone. And don't

worry about me. It's only a scratch. But Colonel Jardine's been hit bad. We'll need bandages."

"And in a hurry, too. I think he's passed out. We've got to stop this damned bleeding," the other soldier said.

Ellen set the lamp down, and stepping away from its circle of light, moved into the shadows. She turned her back on the men. They heard a ripping sound. Ellen had torn wide strips from her petticoat. Blushing furiously, she handed them to the soldier.

"These'll do fine, miss," he said. He worked deftly, bandaging the wound and finishing in a few minutes. He then turned to his companion and examined the man's arm.

"Ain't much, Ralph. You're a lucky one," he said.

Ralph laughed. "Lucky is it?" He turned to Ellen, his eyes twinkling. "You see, miss, that's a soldier's life for you. If you don't get your head blown off, you're lucky. Now, take my friend Walter, here. He got himself one of those little red badges just for standing in the way of a reb ball at Antietam—hardly even got kissed. But me, now—I'll get nothing, not even thanks, because I was hit by a wild-hair donkey in my home town. So I'm lucky and old Walter—he's the hero."

Walter grinned at them. The light shone on the three young faces. And despite the fear that held her, Ellen smiled, too. She was young and the ominous background of war was only a discordant counterpoint which could not entirely blight the exuberance of youth.

In the street, they heard the menacing grumble of the mob as it returned. A hoarse voice yelled, "Some of them bluecoats must be hiding in the houses. Dig 'em out, lads."

"The light——" Walter whispered. Ellen blew out the flame. Walter took the big clasp knife from his pocket and she heard the blade flick open.

Ralph put his hand on her arm. "Easy, miss. If they come—I've got a revolver. We'll take some of 'em. Don't be afraid."

The touch of his hand reassured Ellen. She took a deep breath and made a silent resolution to be brave. . . .

The mob ran from house to house with a great deal of shouting. Pine torches dotted the street and in the smoky glare the faces in the mob took on weirdly shadowed expressions. Men dashed about purposelessly. Women jabbered and chattered. Many of the houses were looted by the rioters. In several instances, residents were dragged out into the street and beaten. After about a half hour of this, the rioters began to weary of the activity and only the most fanatical of them kept up the hunt for hidden soldiers.

Fortunately for the people in 202 East 19th Street, the mob's search had started at the other end of the block and much of the enthusiasm had worn off by the time the rioters reached the house. But, at last, they came. Heavy footsteps sounded outside. Rude fists beat on the door. Ellen and the soldiers froze, while Colonel Jardine, who had regained consciousness, bit his lip to stifle the groans that rose in his throat. Each listened to the noises below.

Julia went to the door and stood in the entranceway against the background of light from within the house.

"What is it? What do you want?" she demanded in a firm voice. She held the revolver concealed in the folds of her voluminous skirt.

"You know damn well. Give up the soldiers," a rioter cried.

"There are no soldiers here," Julia said decisively. She blinked into the glare of torches and in that menacing crowd, spotted a familiar face. She pointed to a young man standing among the rioters, and said, "Dennis McCabe, you know me. I am not against you people. I am a plain widow and my son is home sick from the army. And you, Dennis, coming here like this! Have I not been your mother's friend—and yours? You know that."

Dennis McCabe was a hulking young man whose mother was Julia's laundress. He shuffled uneasily as he remembered Julia's kindness—and the mister's when he'd been alive. Always a gift at Christmas time for Dennis and on his birthday. Always a cup of hot cocoa and a gingerbread cookie on the wintry days when he'd delivered the laundry. His mind was muddled now by all the drinking he'd been doing these past few days—and the fighting. He shook his head. What the hell did a man do? These men were his pals—but Miss Julia was a friend, too.

A bearded man jumped forward and shook his fist in Julia's face. "Out of the way woman or I'll bash your face in," he cried, waving a huge knuckled, hairy paw.

"By Christ, no!" Dennis cried. He grabbed the man by the shoulder and spun him around. "Let her alone! If she says there ain't any soldiers here, then it's the truth. And if you want to make something of it, Grogan—then say the word!"

Grogan scowled at him. The others muttered, hoping these two would fight it out. What a fracas that would be! In his youth Grogan had been a noted brawler, and though he was past forty, his biceps swelled massively and his arms were thickly corded with muscle. Dennis McCabe was a twenty year younger version of Grogan. The older man held his ground for a moment and then said, "Ah, to hell with you, McCabe! You're always ready to jump down a man's throat. But sure, man, it would do no harm if we took a look around in the house, now would it? I'll put it to these lads. Would we be insulting McCabe's friend if we went in for a look?"

"No! No! Grogan's right!" the men yelled.

"Then I'll be the one who does the looking," Dennis said. He had seen what his pals had done to some of the houses on the street.

"Ah, no. None of that. I'm the man who's going inside. We ain't taking chances knowing the way you feel about the missus, here," Grogan said.

"Do as he says, Dennis!" a man shouted.

"No, damn it. No! I'll not have that thieving bastard rob Miss Julia," Dennis cried. He leaped at Grogan. Men seized Dennis and he tried to shake them off. He fought bitterly, but they dragged him away and as they pushed him into the street he cried, "I'm sorry, Miss Julia. I'm sorry!"

Grogan shoved Julia aside and slammed the door behind him. He looked around the place. Then he smiled mockingly at Julia. "You see, lady—I'm a man of my word. I'm the only one who come in. I ain't a bad one. Ask anyone about Tom Grogan. If it's as you say, there's nothing to fear." He walked through the parlor, opening doors and peering into closets. He eyed the stairs. "What's up there?" he asked.

"The bedroom. Nobody is here, I assure you," Julia said easily, her fingers tightening around the revolver butt.

Grogan glanced at the carpeted stairway and then bent closer. He had seen the blood that had dripped from Jardine's wound. The dark stains marked a clear trail in the carpeting. He looked up at Julia with narrowed eyes. "I think I'll take me a look around," he said.

He started for the stairs when Julia swung the revolver up at him. "I think not, Mr. Grogan. Stand where you are."

The big man stopped with one foot on the stairs. A voice from outside called, "Hey, Grogan—we ain't going to wait all night."

"Tell them to go away," she whispered.

He looked into her eyes and saw the cold determination in them. He licked his lips and called, "Then go on, lads. I'll catch up with you."

The men walked off the stoop and there was a sudden out-burst of yelling in the street. A soldier had been caught in an alleyway and the rioters pounced on him like hunting dogs.

"Now, Mr. Grogan," Julia said, pointing to the entrance to the cellar door in the hallway, "please walk toward that door."

He went slowly, his great fists clenching and opening. All at once, the rage within him erupted. He whirled and rushed at Julia. She pulled the trigger. The revolver jumped in her hand. Grogan spun around, then fell heavily against the stairs, killed instantly by the close-range bullet.

The shot brought the two soldiers on the run with Ellen behind them. John clutched the knife and Ralph had the revolver cocked. Ellen leaned over the banister, white and shaken.

"I had to kill him," Julia said.

Ralph stared at the body, as he listened to the clamoring in the street. "I don't think they heard the shot, but we've got to get rid of him," he said.

"You can hide him in the woodpile out in the yard," Julia said. The soldiers lugged Grogan through the kitchen into the backyard. Ellen walked slowly downstairs and stood at the bottom clutching the newel post. She started to cry. Her aunt said sharply, "Stop that, girl. This is no time for tears. I did what had to be done, that's all. It was his life or ours—now get upstairs and look to Colonel Jardine."

Ellen swallowed hard and fought back the tears. "Yes, Aunt Julia," she said.

Her aunt looked at the girl for a moment and said, "Poor Ellen—this has scarcely been a pleasant visit for you."

"It doesn't matter, Aunt Julia. Really it doesn't," Ellen said. And suddenly the pleasure she had been looking forward to on this vacation seemed terribly unimportant. The city, the whole country was in ferment—and at last it had caught up with her. Even gentle people like her aunt had been forced to fight. Well, so could she! And Ellen found that what mattered most to her was to get back to the attic and see that the Colonel was all right. She turned and hurried up the stairs, lifting her skirt so she could run faster.

She sat in the darkness listening to the rasping breathing of the wounded man. She heard the soldiers come back into the house and the sound of their voices as they spoke with her aunt.

Out in the street the mob was still roaring and shouting. Then, suddenly, she heard something else. The strident notes of a bugle. Hoofbeats clattered on the pavement. She rushed to the window and peered out into the dark street. She saw hard-riding horsemen galloping into knots of people, sabers twinkling. The darkness was sliced by the red-orange flashes of cavalry pistols. Rioters were trampled to death by the charging horses. The action on 19th Street was a welter of indistinct figures and blurred patterns of movement.

On the heels of the troopers came a double line of infantry forming a steel-tipped phalanx. Club-swinging police ran along the sidewalks pummeling the rioters left in the wake of the cavalry charge. The mob was routed quickly and thoroughly. On First Avenue the police searched the tenements room-by-room and over the rooftops. Rioters were dragged from hiding places and beaten.

Men came to the house and Ellen heard the door being opened; the excited voices came up to her, the heavy, comforting voices of men. She ran down to the parlor. The room was crowded with uniformed soldiers, and her cousin Jack was with them.

Ellen went to Jack who hugged her. "Mother tells me you were very brave," he said.

"I don't know. I was very frightened. Do you call that being brave?" Ellen asked.

"Everyone is frightened at times like this," Jack said.

It wasn't hard to be brave, Ellen thought. Bravery grew from fear. One was forced into bravery. She had wanted to hide and to weep, but had done neither. This was all part of growing up.

The soldiers crowded around her. Her cheeks glowed with the excitement of attracting so much attention. A team of litter bearers carried Colonel Jardine down. He beckoned to Ellen and when she came to stand by the stretcher, the handsome officer smiled wanly up at her and said, "Thank you, my dear."

Before she could reply, the men carried him off to an army ambulance that had come with the troops. It was decided that Ellen and Julia would be safer in Police Headquarters and a carriage was secured to take them there with the military column. A strong guard of soldiers and police were left to patrol the area.

In the carriage, Ellen leaned against the seat, her eyes closed. Jack and his mother sat opposite. The carriage moved slowly, surrounded by six troopers with drawn sabers. A soldier sat up with the driver, musket ready for instant use. The column moved through riot-torn streets. People stared at it with mute hatred. The soldiers marched in firm ranks, and files of policemen flanked the troops, sharply alert for any overt moves by the sullen onlookers.

The carriage rocked and jolted along and to Ellen, wrapped in the darkness of the coach's interior, the events of the night, of the past few days were like unreal and disjointed segments of troubled dreams. But, actually it had been terribly exciting. She would have much to tell her friends in Boston. It wasn't very likely any of them had been trapped in a house by a howling mob and seen a man shot and torn their petticoats to make bandages for a wounded officer! New York had it all over Boston when it came to excitement: there had been only one feeble protest against the draft at home—a meeting on the Common, quickly dispersed by the police!

5

B Y SOME grapevine, rumors skipped through the city and reached the drinking dives in Five Points, the saloons in Mackerelville, and even skipped up the Island to Yorkville, to Harlem and Manhattanville, that five regiments were enroute from Gettysburg and with them were coming troops of cavalry and batteries of artillery.

The rioters stared gloomily into their whisky glasses. Let the damn bastards come home. There was still time to get a few more niggers before the troops got into the city. There was still time left for arson and robbery—and murder.

And the mobs continued to roam the streets.

A mob tried an attack on Jackson's Foundry located on East 28th Street between First and Second Avenues. They met a roving patrol of soldiers backed by a fieldpiece. A round or so of grape sent the mob flying. But that crowd was not finished with its ugly work.

The tenement house at 147 East 27th Street was inhabited by Negroes. A man named Henry Nichols lived there. He had not ventured out all day for fear of the mobs. His mother, Mrs. Mark Stoat, a seamstress, had spent the day with him and the two had passed the time visiting with neighbors and talking about the riots. Some men in the building formed a defense group to guard the house.

The mob that had been driven from Jackson's Foundry numbered several hundred. The enraged, frustrated rioters took out their feelings in acts of wanton terror. They fired a row of wooden shacks on Second Avenue at 28th Street. Poverty-stricken whites and impoverished Negroes lived in these miserable hovels. This senseless and savage deed was not enough to glut the temper of that mob. It turned into East 27th Street and attacked the Negro tenement building. The few Negroes guarding it put up a fight but were soon overwhelmed. The rioters charged into the place and ran along the hallways, kicking in the doors of apartments.

In one dwelling they came on a young woman lying in bed with her six-day-old baby. Her husband tried to stop them but was killed in cold blood. The blood-lust was raging in the rioters. Wildly glaring men grabbed the screaming woman and flung her through the window into the courtyard below. A man hurled the baby after the mother with the nonchalance he would show in tossing away a cigar butt.

This was only a brief incident in the horror to come. About ten Negroes, mostly women and children and including Mrs. Stoat and her son, managed to reach the basement where they hid themselves in a woodbin and cowered there, listening to the stomping rioters smashing up the apartments on the upper floors.

The rioters were preparing to leave when the frightened group in the cellar was discovered. Instead of storming the basement the whites decided to have some fun. The main water pipe was cut and gallons of water cascaded into the basement. The water soon rose waist deep in the cellar. Women wept and shrieked and clutched their children. The rioters ringed the building and massed in the backyard which had an exit from the basement.

At last, the trapped Negroes could no longer remain where they were. They preferred the risks of a dash out into the darkness to drowning in the cellar. They made a concerted rush for the back door and stumbled out into the weed-choked yard, dripping wet and half mad with fear.

The yard was surrounded by a sagging, rotting picket fence. Several of the women managed to escape, for the few men fought with frenzied courage to give them time. The fight soon ended with the Negroes either killed or knocked unconscious.

Rioters dashed after the fleeing women. Two men caught Mrs. Stoat and dragged her back into the yard. Nichols, bleeding from a dozen wounds, stumbled toward the men who held his screaming, struggling mother.

"Don't harm her. Kill me but don't harm my mother!" he cried.

"Sure, nigger. Glad to oblige. Let the old cow go, boys. We got ourselves a volunteer!" a rioter called out, swinging a crowbar.

The men released Mrs. Stoat who slumped to the ground in a dead faint. Two rioters held Nichols by the arms while the one with the crowbar hefted it and cried, "Watch this, lads! I'll get this nigger with one stroke!"

He raised the bar high and brought it down on Nichols head with full force. There was a sound like a melon bursting open. Nichols was dead before he fell, his head caved in.

Hours later, Mrs. Stoat was found crouching by her son's body in the darkness and moaning unintelligibly, shocked into madness by her ordeal.

Shortly before 10:00 P.M. two bits of information came to Police Headquarters which gladdened every man there. A breathless messenger flung himself from his foam-flecked horse and ran panting up the steps. He shouted out his news in an excited voice,

"The 74th Regiment's coming in from Jersey City!" he yelled. "It's come up from Gettysburg!"

He rushed downstairs into the basement and repeated his tidings. The first of the regiments had returned from Pennsylvania. The men were being loaded onto ferryboats at the Jersey City terminus of the Canal Street ferry and would be arriving in a short time.

General Brown immediately ordered a detail to the ferry dock to act as guides for the arriving regiment. Once more, jubilation broke out in the building. A new spirit gripped everyone. And in addition to the word of the 74th's arrival a telegram came in from the War Department:

War Department
Washington, D.C.
July 15, 1863

Governor Seymour:
Eleven New York Regiments have been relieved and are at Frederick and will be forwarded to New York as fast as transport can be furnished. Please signify anything you may desire to be done by this department. Whatever means are at its disposal shall be at your command for the purpose of restoring order in New York.

Edward Stanton,
Secretary of War

Commissioner Acton smiled appreciatively when Seymour showed him the telegram. At last the burden was being lifted from him. It was good to think the worst was over and that a difficult job had been done successfully.

Mayor Opdyke showed his relief by lighting a cigar. The rich smoke was like a balm in his throat. He rolled the cigar, luxuriating in the taste of it. The Mayor of New York City was no weakling to be pushed around by a pack of dirty necks and their crooked Tammany friends he said to himself with satisfaction. He had a score to settle with the Board of Aldermen and the City Council, too. That damn blackmailing bill of theirs —the dirty cowards expecting the city to pay three hundred dollars for getting some clod out of the draft. He'd veto that bill the minute it reached his desk.

Governor Seymour stood a bit apart and frowned as the others expressed their delight at the telegram. The failure of his speech still rankled. It seemed to him that there were ugly whispers going around. Nothing was said aloud. But he thought Opdyke seemed disdainful and General Brown, brusque and rude. Acton scarcely even looked at him. Even the soldiers and policemen on duty seemed to eye him frostily. He realized now that the riots had actually little to do with the draft law. Certainly the outbreak had come because of the law but once violence was unleashed all principle and purpose vanished. The contradictions within the city—hatreds and economic strife, the putrescence beneath the façade of opulence—came to the surface and became fuel for the riot to feed on.

Seymour now believed he had betrayed himself to the mob by sending his adjutant to Washington to try to have the draft stopped. He should have known mobs are not so easily mollified. Violence spawned violence: at the last, he had been forced to take the very action he most detested. Only force could quell the mobs. The time for reason and logic had gone. It saddened him to admit it.

He glanced about the room, bitterness burning in him like a glowing coal. They were all condemning him because he had spoken like that to the crowd at City Hall—with cautious words, pleading for patience and forbearance. But he had been neither soft nor vacillating with the rioters. He had declared the city in a state of insurrection, had ordered troops out promptly, opened the State Arsenals and worked himself to the point of exhaustion. Yet they hated him because he had called the crowd, "my friends." And even the crowd hated him, branding him a traitor because he had ordered them to disperse and had sent the forces of the state against them.

Yet he felt he was the betrayed, not the betrayer. Those people had been his friends and he had trusted them. My friends, he repeated to himself. The words had lost any real meaning. He had no friends here or anywhere else in this city. His frown deepened and an oppressive sadness engulfed him. Horatio Seymour had learned that civilized and reasonable behavior was no match for bigotry, hatred and brute force.

6

FIVE hundred men of the 74th Regiment, New York State Militia, marched down the gangplanks of the ferryboats that had carried them from Jersey City. Equipment jangled and rattled. Noncoms shouted, their voices rising above the music of a military band tootling a welcome. The soldiers shuffled and shifted, forming into companies after what seemed a welter of impossible confusion.

The troops were grimy and tired from the long train ride, but the men were fit and ready. Their tanned faces could be seen only indistinctly in the uncertain light of kerosene lamps and torches. These veterans had been recruited in far upstate Rochester. Most of them were strangers in New York City, having passed through it only briefly on their way to the war front. They were back now but not as they had wished to return—with furloughs and money.

They glanced about curiously, a little baffled by the apparent calm in the city. According to the rumors, the city should have been smoldering rubble like the devastated towns they had seen lying along the terrible route of war. From where they stood, at the ferry slip, the city seemed to be normal and quiet. There were no signs of destruction and the men decided this was some kind of stupidity dreamed up by that old fox Stanton.

Sure, the War Department couldn't bear to let soldiers sit around and enjoy a little rest after a big battle. Oh, no—that wasn't the way the sons of bitches in Washington worked. And the shoulder straps, too. Old General Meade must have said to himself, now there's the boys of the 74th New York just squatting on their butts. That won't do. Hear there's a little ruckus up in New York City. A couple of drunken donkeys chucking

rocks at the niggers. So the poor 74th had to be loaded on the
trains and sent all the way up here on a wild goose chase.

Being soldiers they grumbled and ranted and acted sullenly.
They swore in low monotonous tones and stood on the pier for
a long time while the officers huddled together and studied
maps in the rays of the bulls' eye lanterns.

After a while the officers trotted back to their companies. A
bugle sounded attention. The staccato notes faded across the
moon-dappled river. The colonel swung onto his horse. He
waved his hand sharply downward. A sergeant major bellowed,
"Fooowad Haaach!"

The color guard paced out and the regiment followed, stepping smartly to the drum's beat while the band on the pier
played "Rally Round The Flag." The 74th marched off to make
a tour of the downtown riot areas. The men saw the ruined
houses in the Negro section where they were greeted with tear-
ful celebration as deliverers. They saw the barricades in the
streets where battles had been fought, and the buildings with
windows and doors splintered by bullets.

They marched for more than an hour through side streets
and along debris strewn avenues. Crowds watched them silently.
Once in a while they heard shouted curses. In scattered places
there was faint applause and thin cheers. But since leaving the
Negro section, the soldiers had met no evidence of friendliness.
To those who had paraded through occupied enemy cities the
reception was a familiar one; the same rebellious crowds eyeing
them with the undisguised hatred they had seen in the South.
By the time the tour was completed not a man doubted the
grimness of the city's ordeal.

A bit sheepishly the soldiers admitted to themselves that
Stanton wasn't a fool and sober-sides Meade knew what he had
been doing. They were really needed up here in New York.

The spirits of the men lifted as the rounds went on. They
understood the purpose of this march. The sight of the disci-

plined regiment marching in unbroken cadence behind the shot-torn flags was a shattering one for the rioters.

The jittery people of New York could rest easily this night—the 74th was in town. As the column headed downtown on Broadway, the command was given to march at ease. A rich baritone voice far up at the head of the regiment started to sing:

> "John Brown's body lies a-moldering in the grave,
> John Brown's body lies a-moldering in the grave,
> John Brown's body lies a-moldering in the grave,
> But his truth goes marching on!"

The men took up the song. They shouted the last line at the top of their youthful voices and the sound of it echoed over Broadway. Hotel guests leaned from upper floor windows and waved handkerchiefs and thundered a joyful welcome. Women tossed flowers to them. Men stood quietly smiling and took off their hats as the Old Flag came by. Hundreds of spectators joined in the singing and the words became a hymn of joy. The truth goes marching on, they sang. The truth goes marching on!

Still, fear slithered through the city like a monstrous snake. In many parts of the sprawling metropolis, looters broke into houses. Arsonists set fires. Murderers struck death blows. But the violence had been blunted. A half hour after the 74th landed, the 65th Regiment, New York State Militia, a Buffalo outfit four hundred strong, came in and was also marched through the stricken areas.

No more did large bodies of rioters move freely through the city. Powerful patrols were out all through the night. Only in the outlying neighborhoods was there still danger.

Yet peace had not fully returned. The rioters were trying to gather new strength and prepare new mischief. A disquietude and a heavy, unnatural silence enveloped the city. As the hours ticked away the tension mounted.

DIMINUENDO

Thursday, July 16, 1863—Friday, July 17, 1863

Thursday

July 16, 1863

. . . 1

A STEAMER nosed its way into a slip at the foot of Canal Street. A line snaked from the boat and was deftly caught by a young sailor on the pier. He flipped it adroitly around a cleat and the boat was fast. The time was 4:00 A.M. The gangplank was lowered and a sleepy band standing by struck up a bedraggled tune. The soldiers began to disembark. They were of New York City's own beloved 7th Regiment. The 7th was home. The Old Guard. Eight hundred city boys had come back and they were fighting mad. They growled at each other as they jostled down the swaying gangplank. Privates snapped at officiously bawling sergeants. The Colonel and his staff stayed off to one side watching the unloading. Sweating details hand-hauled cases of ammunition from the small steamer's deck. The pier was a turbulently busy place.

Somehow, order was established. The troops were brought into line. Despite the early hour it was decided to send the 7th through the East Side streets where bands of hard-drinking roughs were gathered in all-night saloons. The 7th was aching for a scrap and the soldiers glared fiercely at the hostile faces along the way. But there was no fight. The rioters were cowed by the soldiers and made no move or demonstration. Even the drunkest blinked soberly at the lines of soldiers. From daybreak on, all morning long, troops continued to come in.

The most important of the new arrivals was the 69th Regiment, New York State Militia, "The Fighting Irish." The all-Irish unit, whose green flags had been stained with the blood of many battles, longed to tackle a mob. The soldiers were boiling because the rioters had burned the home of their old commander, Colonel Robert Nugent. But they were even angrier that so many of the rioters were Irishmen.

Soldiers of other regiments had taunted the men of the 69th by calling the outbreaks the "Irish Riot." They sneeringly said the Irish were doing the rebels' dirty work in New York City. Brawls had taken place while the 69th was waiting to entrain and soldiers of other regiments bore the marks of battle long before any contact was made with a mob.

When the 69th was paraded through the strongholds of the rioters many in the mob stood ashamed as the tattered green regimental flag went proudly by, waving in the fresh westerly breeze that was dispelling the oppressive heat of the last three days. The "Fighting Irish" marched boldly, in perfect step, behind a band that played old country airs with skirling pipes and booming drums.

It was an auspicious start for a day which saw some semblance of normalcy returning to the city. A streetcar started downtown on Sixth Avenue from the 59th Street depot. Armed soldiers rode the car. It went the length of its run without incident, picking up a few passengers en route. Another car was sent on schedule, then another. The Eighth Avenue line began running again. Omnibuses were rolling, although the public vehicles carried few paying customers. Soon service was nearly normal. Big cavalry patrols with drawn sabers guarded the lines.

Police Headquarters still presented its busy picture. With the arrival of troops, a council-of-war was held by Acton, Opdyke, Brown and Seymour. General Brown, elated by the growing

strength of his command, had a plan for employing the troops
to best advantage. Using the tip of his sword to trace out his
ideas on a map of the city, the General showed how he would
divide New York into four key districts with headquarters in
Harlem, West 22nd Street, East 29th Street and at City Hall.
Each area was to be a mobilization point for a large body of
police and troops while continuous patrols would prevent mobs
from forming.

Having finished his brief lecture, Brown sheathed his sword
and wrinkled his leathery face in a smile. "We've got them, gentlemen. We've got them, now. Do you agree to my plan?"

The others nodded. Acton said, "General, I must make one
request. Place the police in reserve, wherever possible. Most of
my men are worn out and many are wounded but have remained on duty in spite of their injuries. Please use the military for patrols."

"Of course, sir. Shall we put my plan into operation, then?"
General Brown said.

He glanced at Opdyke and the Governor. Opdyke gave his
assent as did Seymour, in a detached, almost disinterested manner. He was eager for the moment when he could leave the city.
All night, he had tossed fitfully in his luxurious quarters at the
St. Nicholas. He felt unwanted and unnecessary and longed to
be back in Albany, immersed in work, insulated from the petty
politicians and self-seeking men who surrounded him here. Not
that there were no hacks on the state level. He had to deal with
many of them. But by shielding himself in the duties of the gov-
ernorship and the dignity of his office, Seymour could erect a
barrier against such men.

Brown strode out to give the necessary orders for transport-
ing and redeploying the troops. Acton dictated telegrams to the
various precincts. Mayor Opdyke sat quietly, smoking his in-
evitable cigar and frowning up at the smoke clouds.

J OHN HUGHES, Archbishop of the New York Diocese of the Roman Catholic Church, was a weary, careworn man. Bedridden by rheumatism, he had suffered far worse than mere physical agonies since the outbreak of the riot. His pain was intense. Spasmodic twinges sent needles of torment through his legs. But the knowledge that many of his parishioners were involved in the uprising brought him anguish that was even more painful.

Hughes knew at firsthand the poverty and sordidness which had evoked the mobs to such unpardonable actions. He did not condone these men and women, and he deplored the murder of innocent Negroes. The Archbishop was a peace-loving man and even the thought of violence revolted him. He hated war, especially this one, which he had publicly branded as unnecessary. Hughes was of the opinion that the southern states should have been permitted to go their paths in peace. Because he felt the draft law would perpetuate the conflict, he opposed that, too.

His antiwar position brought the aged prelate into sharp and acidulous polemics with Horace Greeley. *The Tribune* sniped at him continually in its editorials and when the riots started, Greeley put some of the responsibility for them on the venerable churchman. Greeley claimed that if Hughes had spoken out, he could have stopped the rioters because they were almost exclusively Irish-Catholics and would have listened to him. Other newspapers took the same line.

The ugly affair was not solely the work of either Irishmen or Catholics. Many divergent groups took part. Among the police, volunteers, and military who fought the mobs were thou-

sands of devout Irish-Catholics. In countless cases, parish priests
went into the streets to rescue Negroes and others from violence.
Churches became sanctuaries for mob victims.

In an editorial, *Harper's Weekly* strongly denounced the idea
that the Irish were the sole culprits:

"Some newspapers dwell upon the fact that the rioters were almost
uniformly Irish and hence argue that our troubles arise from the per-
versity of the Irish race. But there have been riots in our time at Paris,
Madrid, Naples, Rome, Berlin and Vienna. Turbulence is no exclusive attribute of the Irish nature. . . . In many wards of the city,
the Irish were stanch friends of law and order. . . . Irishmen helped
rescue the colored orphans in the asylum from the hands of the
rioters . . . a large proportion of the police are Irish and the Roman
Catholic priesthood to a man used its influence on the side of law
and order."

Archbishop Hughes took no active part in the efforts to dis-
suade the rioters from continuing their wild and foolish pattern.
He remained in his home on the northwest corner of 36th Street
and Madison Avenue where many people came and urged him
to add his voice to the protests against the riot and to use his
influence with the rioters.

The Archbishop was reluctant to act, as he felt this was a
matter for the State and not the Church. But as the disorders
continued, Hughes realized he would have to intervene. On
Thursday, all the newspapers, even Greeley's *Tribune,* carried
a pastoral letter from the prelate. It said:

AN APPEAL TO THE IRISH CATHOLICS FROM
ARCHBISHOP HUGHES:

In the present disturbed state of the city, I will appeal not only
to them, but to all persons who love God and profess to respect also
the laws of man and the peace of society, to retire to their homes with
as little delay as possible, and disconnect themselves from the seem-
ingly deliberate attempts to disturb the peace and social rights of
the citizens of New York.

+ John, Archbishop of New York

In addition to this letter, Hughes had the town placarded with a poster which announced that he would address a meeting at 2:00 P.M. on Friday from the balcony of his home. He explained that he would do so while seated, since rheumatism prevented him from standing. He also promised that anyone attending the meeting would not be molested by police or the military.

Wherever the poster had been put up, crowds formed to read it and the letter in the newspapers was eagerly perused. The newspaper which had most actively supported the rioters—*The New York Daily News*, edited by Ben Wood—gave great prominence to the letter. Even Ben Wood had grown squeamish over the excesses of the mobs. He felt that Hughes' message might help bring the disorders to an end; he was well aware of the efforts being made by city, state and federal authorities to find a connection between Ben Wood, his brother Fernando, and the rioters. However, the most thorough investigation had turned up no evidence that the Woods were in collusion with the rioters, although there were whispers, rumors, and innuendoes to that effect.

In the wealthy homes of men who hated Lincoln and the Union, there were furtive sighs of relief when Archbishop Hughes' letter appeared. Now, they felt, the whole business would end. The Irish would listen to their Archbishop and the rabble would slink back into the slums.

These sanctimonious men who had lighted the fires that heated the eruption sat in their parlors and smoked their expensive Havanas. But somehow, the cigars did not taste good and the fine breakfast coffee was bitter. They were bound to each other by a cord of treason and if that delicate cord broke in any one place all would be dragged to disgrace and ruin.

Alone, each man turned his searching thoughts inward. Each wondered about the other and the weaknesses that might give way to the pressures of conscience and guilt. They were on the brink, these wealthy and prominent men, trapped in a terror of their own making, an endless purgatory of mutual distrust. They had grown to despise each other but were bound into associations they could never relinquish for fear of betrayal.

The publication of the Archbishop's letter did not have the immediate effect for which the prelate had hoped. The reactions of the rioters were mixed. The bitterest called Hughes a traitor and complained he had no right to interfere. Others defended him and fights erupted between the factions. The violence the prelate abhorred broke out anew. His peacemaking attempt had aroused fresh antagonisms.

. . . *3*

A POIGNANT reminder of the mob's brutality was seen at an early hour Thursday morning. Many of the children from the Colored Orphan Asylum had been comfortably housed in the City Orphanage on the Bloomingdale Road in the upper part of Manhattan. But about one hundred had been given only haphazard temporary shelter in whatever places the police could find on short order.

Acton had not forgotten these unfortunate children. He arranged to have them transported to Blackwell's Island where good facilities were available for them in a wing of the City Hospital. Accordingly, as soon as they could be spared, fifty policemen were detailed to the task of escorting the orphans to this destination. Chattering happily, the children seemed to have forgotten their grim ordeal. They walked through the street, hand in hand, guarded by the police. People watched the procession and some shouted and shook their fists but none dared make a move toward the children.

A small steamer was awaiting them at the foot of East 35th Street. The orphans were marched aboard and the boat pulled away toward Blackwell's Island. The children lined the railing and began to sing as though it were a festive picnic party.

The day started at Police Headquarters with an attitude of confidence. General Brown's plan had been put into effect and the morning was spent sending troops and their equipment to various parts of the city.

A force of policemen crowded aboard Police Steamboat No. 1 for a tour of outlying areas. They landed at Flushing, Astoria, Ravenswood and other points where outbreaks had been reported. The men of the 23rd Precinct were sent back to Yorkville by boat. When they docked at the foot of East 86th Street, relieved residents greeted them warmly.

Led by Captain Henry Hutchings, the officers marched through Yorkville's streets searching for the rioters who had destroyed the precinct house and many private dwellings. But word of their arrival had preceded the police. The rioters cleared out of Yorkville and, after three days, peace was at last restored to the area.

The troops were soon deployed as General Brown wanted them. Patrols went out in all districts and, apparently, the situation was in hand. For many minutes, the telegraph keys in Police Headquarters were silent and not a single report of trouble came over the wires.

But the peaceful hiatus did not last long. Omnibuses and streetcars trying to negotiate Second Avenue were stoned by a crowd of several hundred near 30th Street. Passengers and drivers were forced to flee. The abandoned vehicles were immediately set on fire and once more yowling mobs danced around

the bonfires. Second Avenue swarmed with rioters who were
out for all the trouble they could find.

A patrol of dismounted cavalrymen of about platoon strength
and armed with repeating carbines came into contact with the
mob. There was a short fight and in a matter of minutes the
soldiers were in complete retreat. A sergeant was struck on the
head by a thrown rock and killed by the blow. His body lay in
the gutter on East 28th Street.

Children, egged on by their mothers, took the dead man's
boots, stripped him of his clothing and left the corpse naked.
The women gathered around to stare at the body, laughing and
making lewd jokes, until someone who had a semblance of de-
cency covered the corpse with a blanket.

And while the women performed their ghoulish rites, the
rioters pursued the soldiers, who scattered in all directions.
About twenty-five of them took refuge in Jackson's Foundry on
East 28th Street. The sturdy brick building, with its ponderous
doors and small round windows, was an ideal fortress for the
embattled soldiers.

The first onrush by the mob was stopped by a fusillade from
the carbines. The rioters retired a block or so, carrying their
wounded with them. They decided the best way to get at the
soldiers was to smoke them out. Someone suggested loading
wagons with hay, pouring kerosene over the bales and then
rolling the blazing wagons up against the building. Rioters ran
off eagerly to get the required materials.

The young captain who had been in command of the patrol
found a horse and rode at full gallop to Police Headquarters.
He reported to General Brown and told him what had happened.
Brown fixed the pale officer with a baleful glare.

"And what the devil are you doing here, sir?" he bellowed.

"I've come to make my report, sir," the captain stammered.

"Damn it, man! You belong with your troops! An officer's
place is with his men!"

"But, sir—the report—"

"I don't care a pinch of cowshit about the report. Any damn fool private could have brought the message! Now get the hell back to your command!" Brown roared.

The crestfallen officer looked about him helplessly. His youthful face was screwed up as though he was about to cry. He walked slowly through the suddenly silent basement. Everyone watched him trudging up the stairs, head bent, his sword slapping against the balustrade.

Brown shook his head as he glanced over at Acton. "Don't know what ails these kids. They just don't make soldiers any more," he said. He shrugged. "An officer belongs with his men, not sniveling around Headquarters. I'll send Captain Putnam and a company of regulars. This is a job that needs real soldiers. Putnam will know how to deal with this scum."

"Inspector Carpenter can spare men to send along," Acton said.

Brown nodded and went out, pulling his cap lower over his eyes. Acton looked after him and said, "That man lives on blood and thunder. I think he's actually going to be sorry when it's over."

"We owe him a lot. He's done a good job," Mayor Opdyke said. He turned to Governor Seymour. "Don't you think so, Governor?"

Seymour, who had been staring moodily at the wall, looked at the Mayor, "I beg your pardon, Mayor Opdyke, I wasn't listening."

"I said General Brown has done a good job. Don't you agree?"

"Oh, yes. Indeed he has." And what if he had said no he didn't think so? They'd have been ready to leap on his words and twist them. Brown deserved no medals. He was a soldier and had done his work as a soldier should. And he had used soldiers' tools—grapeshot and bullets and bayonets—not words and logic and ideas. And the pity of it was that General Brown's way was the only one to follow.

Opdyke noticed how gray-faced and haggard the Governor looked. Seymour seemed to have aged years in these few days. The Mayor was an astute, rather than understanding, man—but he felt keenly at the moment for Seymour. He could see how sharp the Governor's disappointment had been at the failure of his speech and he knew, too, that Seymour's only mistake had been to employ the wrong weapon in this battle. Men like Brown were needed for such work. He walked to Seymour's side and laid a friendly hand on the Governor's shoulder.

"If I may say it, sir, you've done a good job, too. Our state is fortunate to have a man like you at its helm," he said.

Seymour looked up and for a moment searched for the mockery in Opdyke's eyes. There was only sincerity. Opdyke was a shrewd and wily merchant but also a man who was capable of genuine feeling and this was such a time for him.

"Thank you," Seymour said, a little embarrassed by his emotions. The friendly words cheered him.

Opdyke reached up to his breast pocket, took out his cigar case and offered one to the Governor. "I find, Governor Seymour, that there is much comfort in a good cigar," he said.

Seymour rarely smoked but this time he did not refuse. He took the panatela. The Mayor struck a match, lit the Governor's cigar and then his own. The men smoked quietly and comfortably. Opdyke, with his hands clasped behind his back, teetered to and fro on his heels. Seymour sat down in a straight-backed chair. The cigar smoke curled about their heads and drifted to the ceiling. Telegraph keys clacked away. Outside, the muffled voices of sergeants could be heard shouting orders, which were followed by the tread of marching men. Captain Putnam's punitive force had started out and the cycle of violence was beginning again.

Shortly after the joint police-military expedition had commenced to trek uptown, Police Superintendent John Kennedy arrived at Police Headquarters in a carriage. He had spent two days in New York Hospital recovering from the beating he had received on Monday. His face was still marked with swollen bruises and purplish welts. He stepped stiffly from the carriage, leaning heavily on a cane, and limped up the stairs. He moved haltingly, like an old man, with no trace of his former jauntiness.

Dan Carpenter was talking to Inspector George Dilks at the top of the stairs. The men hurried to Kennedy. He spoke to them in a shaking voice. They recalled the incisive bite of his tones and felt pity for this fumbling, weary stranger, but neither man revealed to him or to each other that he noted any change. To them, he was still Superintendent Kennedy. They walked with him down the long corridor. Policemen greeted Kennedy with warm respect. As he entered the basement, all work stopped. The men crowded around him to shake his hand and after looking into his battered face, turned away with anger in their eyes.

When he confronted Governor Seymour, Kennedy apologized for his absence from duty. "I'm ready now, sir," he said.

Seymour cleared his throat uneasily. He weighed his words with care. It was obvious that Kennedy was not in condition to resume the arduous work that still lay ahead, and despite Seymour's personal feelings about the man, Tom Acton had been superb.

"Superintendent, we're delighted to have you back with us. I'm sure it will not take you very long to acquaint yourself with the dispositions that have been made to meet the situation. We'll be glad for your help," the Governor said.

Kennedy twisted his puffed lips into a smile. "You've done fine without me, sir. I know you don't need me. But, gentlemen, if you don't mind, I'd like to stay and look on."

"You'll do more than look on. I've needed you every minute," Acton said.

The others all murmured agreement and Kennedy thanked them. He had come to Headquarters against the doctor's orders on his release from the hospital because he needed the reassurance that he was not merely a broken, pain-wracked old man who would take months to mend physically and even longer to lose the memory of what had happened to him. He wanted to be in this Headquarters, where he belonged. He had needed to hear them say he was missed. Now, he was content to take a seat at the long table and keep out of the way as busy men hurried about. He leaned on the cane, chin resting on his folded hands, and studied the scene through bloodshot, swollen eyes.

. . . *4*

THE siege of Jackson's Foundry was turning out to be more fun than a circus. Wagons, loaded with blazing hay were sent caroming toward the squat building from the corner of Second Avenue and East 28th Street. The street sloped sharply enough to roll the vehicles downhill.

The rioters hauled wagons from blocks around. They secured the hay by raiding nearby livery stables. With much yelling and boisterous activity, the wagons were dragged into place and aimed at the foundry which stood midway between First and Second Avenues. The bales of hay were ignited and the wagons sent rattling at the buildings. Some of the vehicles stalled and burned to the cobblestones. Others veered off and turned over, spreading flaming brands of hay everywhere. A vagrant wind picked up the blazing pieces and dropped them on surrounding housetops. Soon, several shacks in East 28th Street caught fire.

The foundry was unharmed. Only one wagon managed to reach the building. It crashed into a wall, bounced off, toppled over on its side and burned merrily. The rioters' strategy had failed. The only way to get at the soldiers was to attack them. This, the mob was disinclined to attempt. The rioters milled about, frowning at the building. The soldiers couldn't leave. That was certain. The mob had the place hemmed in. But the carbines that poked out the porthole windows were too deadly for the rioters to try a rush.

After some wrangling back and forth, the mob appointed a committee led by a stringy man, who wore a battered plug hat and a motley uniform of army pants tucked into cavalry boots, a bright red Zouave blouse and a multicolored bandana around his neck. He had the appearance of a vivid scarecrow. Somehow, he had supplied himself with a navy cutlass to which he had tied a dirty white piece of rag as a flag of truce.

Accompanied by a score of drunken ruffians, the skinny leader marched his deputation to the gates of the foundry. Waving his soiled truce banner, he called out, "Hey, in there! We won't do you no hurt! Throw out your guns and we'll let you go on your way. If not, we'll come in and drag you out!"

Some of the soldiers barricaded in the foundry were regulars and the rest had seen hard fighting in Virginia and elsewhere. The ranking trooper was a tough old top sergeant named Charles Mercier. He had twenty years of service behind him during which he had fought against Indians, Mexicans and Confederates. He had no intention of surrendering to this mob. His men were well-armed with forty rounds of ammunition each and Spencer carbines. He grinned tightly. There was always time to worry about giving up when the ammunition ran out.

The man in the plug hat shouted, "What's your answer? This is your last chance!"

Mercier raised his carbine and took careful aim. "Here it is, you son of a bitch," he yelled.

He pressed the trigger. The rioter's hat flew from his head with a neat hole just above the hair line. Mercier put his face to the window and shouted, "You've got just ten seconds to clear out, you bastards!"

The delegation fled without ceremony and the leader flung away his sword as he ran with long, clumsy strides. He did not stop for his hat, either, and it lay on the ground, a forlorn symbol of its wearer's fleeting moment of importance.

Mercier turned to his men. "They'll be coming now, lads," he said.

A soldier idly spat a full stream of tobacco juice against the wall and watched it trickle down. "Let 'em come, sarge. We've got to do something to earn the sixteen dollars the guv'mint pays us every month."

The mob attacked the foundry three times. Each was a mad, surging rush aimed at overwhelming the defenders. The carbines cracked away briskly with good effect. Four dead men were crumpled in the gateway. Among them was the erstwhile committee leader, his crimson blouse wet with his blood.

The mob's temper was aroused. Those rioters who had weapons sniped away at the windows. Bullets zipped and ricocheted off the foundry's walls. One rioter, bolder and luckier than the rest ran a zigzag course through the gateway, hurtling over the bodies of his mates. He tossed a bottle of Greek fire through a lower window and got away under a hail of carbine bullets. The Greek fire smashed on the stone floor and the noxious liquid soaked a pile of cotton waste material as it burst into flame.

Five soldiers had to fight the fire. They formed a bucket line, dipping water from a cistern inside the plant. But while they were battling the blaze, the mob re-formed for another charge. Without the guns of the missing troopers the fire power of the defenders was weakened enough to permit dozens of rioters to get into the courtyard. They started battering down the main door.

At this most critical moment, Captain Putnam arrived. His regulars swung into action. An aimed volley and a bayonet charge drove the rioters away from the building. Four pieces of artillery accompanied Putnam. He put two of the guns to work at once shelling the rioters concentrated on Second Avenue. When the mob had been broken up by the grapeshot, fifty policemen who had come along went in with their sticks.

The police assault was the last act in the battle of Jackson's Foundry. The rioters fled. Surveying the situation, Captain Putnam saw that all resistance had been broken. Since there was no further need for his troops, he detached twenty men and a sergeant to patrol the area and reinforced them with the police detail. The rest of the troops returned to Headquarters. After the dead and wounded had been removed, quiet settled over the neighborhood which drowsed in the bright afternoon as though the fight had never occurred.

All through the day and even after darkness fell there were no further alarms. The men at Police Headquarters had time to rest. Telegraphers dozed in their chairs. Crews went out to make permanent repairs on the lines. No one molested them at their work even though it took them into mob-controlled areas like Five Points and Mackerelville. The soldiers who went along as guards had little to do but smoke their pipes and lounge in the repair wagons.

Commissioner Acton retired to a reserve room upstairs and went to sleep on a cot, leaving Carpenter in charge. Superintendent Kennedy had been escorted to his home. Governor Seymour and Mayor Opdyke left for dinner at the St. Nicholas. The Governor went to his room early. Opdyke found friends and whiled away the hours playing poker in his suite.

Strong patrols roved the streets and there were dozens of minor clashes as incipient mobs were broken up as they formed.

But the fight at Jackson's Foundry was the last of any importance.

A sudden summer rainstorm broke over the city with rending thunderclaps and blinding flashes of lightning. Rain swept down in driving sheets and the rivers were churned into white-capped frenzy. But the storm did not halt the arrival of more troops. Far into the night, fresh regiments of infantry, cavalry and artillery came into the city. The men and animals sloshed through rain-drenched streets to Police Headquarters where hot food and dry shelter awaited them.

That night, the only violence in New York City was the violence of nature. It seemed that men had had enough.

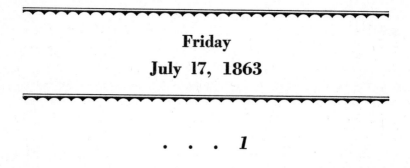
. . . *1*

THE storm died before dawn, which came up with cheerful promise in a burst of red and orange. The sky was fresh and unclouded. The trees and lawns revived by the rain were crisply green in the sunlight. Raindrops and dew formed a translucent cover in the vales and farmlands and the sunlight reflected tiny rainbows in the water.

Soldiers grouped about field kitchens for their morning coffee, chatting and laughing with the bubbling humor of youth.

The ferries from Brooklyn and Jersey poked cautious noses into the slips. A few hardy passengers ventured timorously down the ramps as if expecting disaster to strike at any moment. The city seemed normal. Carts and drays were moving along the docks. Gangs of longshoremen, many of whom bore the marks of battle, appeared at the shape-up.

No one had to spread the news that the city was no longer dangerous. The next ferries were packed with passengers coming in for their day's work. Factory workers and clerks were jammed together on the decks looking eagerly toward Manhattan.

Only the Negroes were absent from the streets. They were still skulking in the deep woods to the north, manning their rifle pits in Eastern District, or crouching behind flimsy barricades in the Negro quarter, waiting and determined to die with courage.

Crowded omnibuses rolled down the avenues, passengers gawking at the ruins and the havoc wrought during the bloody days. Sheepish factory workers stood at the locked gates waiting for the foremen to open shop. They avoided each other's eyes and did not speak much as though a shame they barely understood had clamped a thick hand over their lips.

The shops on Broadway opened. Storekeepers ruefully eyed the wreckage of their establishments. One enterprising merchant who sold combs and brushes on Broadway near 28th Street put up a crudely lettered sign on the front of his fire-charred store:

> Our goods are damaged by fire
> And also blackened by smoke.
> Won't you please buy 'em,
> So we don't go broke!

Housewives came out into the summer morning with shopping baskets and trooped to inspect the scanty stocks in the produce markets. By midmorning, long convoys of farm wagons laden with vegetables rolled into the city. The slaughter houses on the West Side which had suspended operations since Monday went back into business. Even in Allerton's ruined stockyard by the gutted remains of the Bull's Head Hotel, drovers brought in cattle herds and butchers started bidding for the stock.

The pulse of the city grew steadily stronger. Work crews were busy with hammers and saws and lumber at the burned buildings. Construction gangs toiled in the ruins of the State Armory, shoveling debris into barrels and clearing away the rubble. The gutted walls of the Provost Marshal's Office were torn down, and already surveying teams were staking out the boundaries of a new building.

William Davis, Superintendent of the Colored Orphan Asylum, and members of his staff poked about in the blackened heap of the destroyed home and talked about plans for a larger and finer structure.

The tempo picked up as the day grew older and the rumble of wheels in the busy streets drowned out the menacing growls of the still mutinous and disgruntled thousands who had lost their fight and succeeded only in feeding, for a brief time, the fires of treason.

For the first time in almost a week, Mayor Opdyke was seated at his desk in City Hall. The quiet dignity of the room gave him a feeling of well-being, a sense of normalcy. Earlier, he had gone to his house accompanied by Sergeant Young and several detectives. What he had seen there made him understand even more acutely the danger that had been threatening the city.

Although the attack on his house had been repelled before any serious damage could be inflicted, the mob had done enough. Windows were shattered. The flower garden had been trampled. The interior of the house had been spared although paint had been chipped from the parlor walls where rocks had come in through the windows. A squad of police guarded the premises.

After his visit home, the Mayor drove back to City Hall and closeted himself in his office. His first act had been to veto the bill the Aldermen and City Council had passed the previous day. No man was going to have his exemption fee paid by New York City! Having done this, the Mayor wrote a proclamation stating that the riots were over and that enough military force was on hand to forestall any illegal manifestations. He called for discipline and assured the citizens life would be protected and property respected.

He rang a push-bell standing on the desk and a sallow-faced spectacled clerk nervously entered the office. He was not the regular man, but one the Mayor had never noticed before.

Opdyke handed him the sheet. "I want this printed on placards and prominently posted all over the city. Copies will be sent to the newspapers."

"Yes, sir," the clerk said. "Your Honor——?"

"Yes?"

"Is it really over? I mean, sir, are we safe now? It was terrible up in Yorkville—where I live, sir. Terrible."

"I know. But there's nothing more to fear. We have eleven regiments in the city. I'm certain the riot is broken."

"I hope so, sir. Me and the missus was that scared. And us, with a houseful of colored folks."

"What's that?"

"Well, sir, we hid ten of 'em. Since Monday night. I said to the missus we can't let those poor people be butchered before our eyes. So we hid them. Me and the missus, we sat up on the porch with the shotguns, and the rioters never bothered us at all."

Opdyke looked at the nondescript clerk with respect. He rose and extended his hand, "I want to shake your hand, sir. If we had more men like you in our city the riot would never have happened," he said.

The clerk took his hand, timidly. "I'm proud of you," the Mayor said.

"Thank you, sir," the clerk said. He smiled with confusion and walked out of the room, his eyes misting behind his glasses, his heart filled with the glory of the moment.

After he left, Opdyke remembered he didn't know the man's name. But these were the real heroes, the little people, the faces in the crowd one saw and forgot. The Mayor sat down in his comfortable chair and turned it so he could look out over the Park. The fountain was sending up its gossamer spray and the lawn was smooth and green. A company of soldiers was drilling. Birds twittered in the trees and sunlight formed a filigree of shadow as it filtered through the leaves.

The Mayor was well pleased; he had shown everyone that

George Opdyke was a man of courage, whose strength came from within himself and not from the material things his money could buy.

Police Headquarters was still crowded and the streets around were filled with military movements; there was no longer strain and anxiety apparent there. General Brown still kept mounted pickets on duty and had sentries manning guard posts, but everyone knew the rioters had been beaten and the riots quashed.

Policemen who had borne the major part of the fighting strutted about with a swagger and those who had been slightly wounded wore their bandages as badges of honor.

There was still work for the police to do. Squads went out into the rookeries of Five Points, the squatters' shacks by the river fronts and the jumbled East side tenements to search for loot taken during the riots.

They found trunks filled with costly linens and chests of silverware buried in the filth of Five Points cellars. Damask tablecloths, cut glass pitchers, fine decanters were recovered in stinking shacks where goats and pigs wandered around the garbage littered yards. Suits, neckties, shirts and shoes stolen from Brooks Brothers were wrested from the thieves. Costly rosewood furniture was piled up in black hole tenement rooms.

Detectives made the rounds of hockshops and fences. A mountain of stolen jewelry, watches, rings and other valuables was recovered in these places. Notices were printed in the newspapers advising anyone who had suffered losses to examine the property at Police Headquarters and on proving ownership to reclaim their belongings.

The basement of Police Headquarters that had been the nerve center of the city's defense was almost deserted. A sleepy telegrapher sat alone at the rows of keys and only a few policemen were on duty. But the floor, littered with cigar butts, pipe ashes and tobacco juice was evidence of the many people who had been there only hours before. Acton was at home for a deserved rest. Governor Seymour had departed from the city on an early train for Albany. Hawley, the Chief Clerk, Crowley, the Telegraphic Bureau Supervisor, the inspectors and other officials were gone, too.

A single key clacked away making a tiny noise in the huge room. The telegrapher yawned, waved his hand at a fly that was buzzing about his head and lethargically took down the routine message coming off the wire.

. . . **2**

LONG before 2:00 P.M. a crowd started collecting under the balcony of the brick house on the northwest corner of Madison Avenue and 36th Street, the residence of Archbishop Hughes. The people came in solemn, plodding columns and stood placidly on the corner. As the numbers increased, the crowd spread across the roadway and into the empty lots on the block. They had come to hear their Archbishop and were dressed in the clothes they wore to church; the men in rusty black suits shiny from wear and the women in clean unstylish dresses. Even the raggedy children had been scrubbed and wore presentable clothes.

It was hard to believe this orderly, drab crowd had made up the swollen, raging mobs which had held the city in a grip of terror. But men with bloodied bandages about their heads, arms in slings, with swollen, welted faces, were numerous in that crowd. They stood now, like chastised drunkards, with bowed heads, awaiting the scolding of their father.

No sign of police or soldiers was anywhere near that vast throng. The Archbishop had kept his word that no one would interfere with the visit to their prelate. Some blocks away, a dozen troops of cavalry were mounted. Artillery batteries were hitched and waiting. Infantry and police were mobilized. They were out of the crowd's sight, but a system of signals had been arranged with detectives who were mingling in the crowd. If there was any disturbance, the forces would be sent into action.

At precisely 2:00 P.M. Archbishop Hughes appeared on the balcony. Assisted by two young priests, he walked with difficulty to a chair that had been put in place for him by the balcony railing. A great shout went up from the people when they saw Hughes. He seated himself, raised both hands for silence, and in a strong, resonant voice, surprising from one who seemed so frail, the Archbishop began to speak. He spoke long and eloquently, with many humorous and earnest appeals to national pride and religious feeling. His address was full of good counsel and a sort of fatherly indignation.

He said in part:

"Every man has the right to defend his house or his shanty at the risk of life. The cause, however, must be just. It must not be aggressive or offensive. Do you want my advice?"

"Yes! Yes!" the onlookers cried.

"Then I will give it to you. I have been hurt by reports that you were rioters. You cannot imagine that I could hear these things without being grievously pained. Is there not some way you can stop these proceedings and support the laws, none of which have been enacted against you as Irishmen and Catholics?

"You have suffered already. No government can save itself unless it protects its citizens. If military force is turned on you again, the innocent are likely to be shot down and the guilty escape. Would it not be better to retire quietly?"

His speech was over. With the aid of the two priests, he rose and blessed the gathering and went back into the house. Something like a sigh went up from the crowd. The people walked slowly away. . . .

Bibliography
July, 1863

Books:

Asbury, Herbert   The Gangs of New York—N.Y.: A. A. Knopf, 1929
Ye Olde Fire Laddies—N.Y.: A. A. Knopf, 1930

Barnes, David   The Draft Riots of New York—N.Y.: Baker & Goodwin, 1863

Brace, Charles Loring   The Dangerous Classes of New York—N.Y.: Wynkoop & Hallenbeck, 1872

Browne, Junius Henri   The Great Metropolis, A Mirror of New York—Hartford, Conn: American Publishing Company, 1869

Campbell, Helen   Daylight and Darkness—Hartford, Conn: A. D. Worthington, 1892

Costello, A. E.   Our Firemen—N.Y.: Knickerbocker Book Publishing Company, 1888

——————   Our Police Protectors—N.Y.: F. Roper & Company, 1885

Hardee, W. J.	Elementary Instructions In The School of The Soldier—N.Y.: M. Doolady, 1851
————————	Rifle and Light Infantry Tactics— Philadelphia: Lipincott, Grambo & Company, 1855
Harris, Charles Townsend	Memories of Manhattan in the 60's and 70's—N.Y.: The Derrydale Press, 1928
Headley, John Wm.	Confederate Operations in New York and Canada—N.Y.: Neale Publishing Company, 1906
Headley, Joel Tyler	The Great Riots of New York, 1712-1871.—N.Y.: E. B. Treat, 1873
Milton, George Fort	Lincoln and The Fifth Column— Washington, D.C.: The Infantry Journal, 1943
Shannon, Fred Albert	Organization and Administration of the Union Army—Cleveland: The Arthur H. Clark Company, 1928
Stoddard, William O	The Volcano Under The City— N.Y.: Fords, Howard & Hulbert, 1887
Walling, George	Recollections of a New York Chief of Police—N.Y.: Caxton Book Concern, Ltd., 1887
Wiley, Bell Irvin	The Life of Billy Yank—N.Y.: Bobbs-Merrill Company, 1951

Periodicals (July-August, 1863)

Harper's Weekly
Leslie's Weekly
New York Illustrated News
London Illustrated News

Newspapers (July, 1863)

Brooklyn Daily Eagle, The
Freeman's Journal and Catholic Register, The
Irish-American, The
Journal of Commerce, The
New York Argus, The
New York Caucasian, The
New York Copperhead, The
New York Daily News, The
New York Herald, The
New York Ledger, The
New York Evening Post, The
New York Sun, The
New York Sunday Dispatch, The
New York Times, The
New York Tribune, The
New York World, The

Magazine Articles

Brownson, Orestes A. Catholics and the Anti-Draft Riots—
  N.Y.: Brownson's Quarterly Review,
  October, 1863
Hoffman, Henry B. Changed House Numbers and Lost
  Street Names—N.Y.: New-York His-
  torical Society Quarterly Bulletin,
  Vol. 21
Leonard, Ellen Three Days Reign of Terror—N.Y.:
  Harper's Magazine, January, 1867
Man, Albon P. The Church and The New York Draft
  Riots—Philadelphia: American Cath-
  olic Historical Society of Philadel-
  phia, Records, March, 1951

——————— Labor Competition and the New York Draft Riots—N.Y.: Journal of Negro History, October, 1951

Meehan, Thomas F. Archbishop Hughes and the Draft Riots —N.Y.: U.S. Catholic History Society, Records and Studies, Vol. 1, 1900

Pamphlets, Guidebooks and Directories

Eyewitness Accounts Bloody Week, The—N.Y.: Contant & Baker, 1863

Colyer, Vincent To The Memory of the Martyrs—N.Y.: V. Colyer, 1863

Daggett's New York City Street Directory—N.Y.: 1863

Miller's New York As It Is—N.Y.: 1863

Report of the Committee of Merchants for The Relief of Colored People Suffering from the Late Riots—N.Y.: G. A. Whitehorn, 1863

Seymour, Vallandigham and the Riots of 1863—N.Y.: n.p. 186-?

Trow's Directory, 1863—N.Y.: 1863

Valentine's Manual, 1863—N.Y.: 1863